STROUD 'S
BIRTHPLACE

DIANE HARRIS AND TRACY SPIERS

First published November 2003
Copyright (c) Diane Harris and Tracy Spiers, 2003

Published by: EPE Books, Highcroft, South Woodchester, GL5 5EP

ISBN 0-9533979-3-9

Edited by Mike Harris

Designed by gedesign, Spring Cottage, Harley Wood, Nailsworth, GL6 0LB

Printed by Cotswold Printing Company

Front cover photo by Matthew Bigwood

With special thanks, this book is dedicated to
Pat and Tod
Jan and Bruce
and all other mums and dads without whom...

Laurie Lee pictured with his wife Kathy and daughter Jessy, who was born at Stroud Maternity in 1963 Picture reproduced with kind permission of Kathy Lee

All profits from the sale of this book will go towards Stroud Maternity's bid to gain the UNICEF and World Health Organisation's Baby Friendly Hospital Initiative, a global campaign to establish best practice in breastfeeding.

CONTENTS

FOREWORD

by Dr Mark Porter

I FIRST SET FOOT in Stroud Maternity Hospital on March 10, 1989, not as a doctor but as a proud new father of Charlotte, and the process was repeated with the birth of my second daughter, Sarah, the following year.

Four years later, in 1993, I officially opened the newly upgraded post-natal area, which included refurbishment of the delivery suite and main ward. Unveiling the commemorative wall plaque, with my name on it, in front of colleagues was one of the most toe-curlingly embarrassing things I've done!

But my most vivid memory by far is the night I had to carry out a forceps delivery while being photographed by the father-to-be who worked for a local newspaper.

It was the first forceps delivery I had done for years and I am still not sure who was more scared: the parents, the midwife or me.

Fortunately, it all went to plan and ended happily. The family are still patients of mine and the mum is now a local midwife.

It is obvious from the contributions in this book that the unit has touched the lives of many other patients and staff over the years. Much may have changed since it first opened in 1953, but I am pleased to say Stroud Maternity remains just as important a part of our community in its 50th year as it always has been.

INTRODUCTION

STAGGERING CHANGES have taken place since Stroud Maternity Hospital first opened its doors in 1953, at a time when most births occurred at home.

In the 50 years since, however, one thing has remained constant – the incredible level of care given to the thousands of mothers and children who have been looked after there. Time with babies is so precious and brief. Those magical first few days of life with a newborn need time and space to be appreciated.

The unit is one of the few sanctuaries left which really values that time. A host of characters have worked there, ranging from midwives, doctors and obstetricians to nursing auxiliaries and many other support staff, and all have played a vital role in the lives of parents and children in the Stroud district.

This book is a tribute to their dedication and hard work and a celebration of the new lives which have been given such a gentle, caring start. We hope it gives a glimpse into the lives of those connected with the unit and paints a vivid picture of its first 50 years.

A view of Stroud Maternity Hospital

COMPLETED AT LAST: STROUD'S MATERNITY HOSPITAL

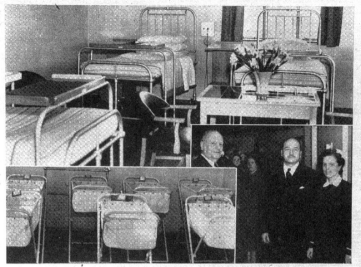

THE LIGHT AND AIRY appearance of the interior of the new hospital is apparent in the photographs of one of the five-bedded wards (top) and of the nursery. Mr. H. G. Tanner, chairman of the Regional Board, who opened the new building, is shown with Col. H. A. Guy (centre), chairman of the Management Committee, and the new Matron (Miss I. Haskins).

"THIS is absolutely marvellous," was the phrase constantly being used by members of the large crowd which filled the rooms and passage ways at Stroud's new Maternity Hospital when it was opened officially on Monday. Considerable public disquiet has been felt at the delays in getting the new building open, but all who have been able to inspect its interior, are agreed that the town and district is extremely fortunate in having such a magnificent addition to its hospital services.

The fact that the Hospital is now open for use put everyone present at Monday's ceremony in to a good frame of mind, which was reflected by the remarks of the chairman of the South Western Regional Hospital Board (Mr. H. G. Tanner), who performed the opening ceremony. He asked his hearers not to consider too much the vicissitudes through which the plans had passed but to rejoice in the fact that the building was at last ready for use.

TWENTY-THREE BEDS

Twenty-three beds are available for use in the new building. There are two five-bedded wards, one double ward and the remainder single rooms. Provision has been made for two private wards which can be booked in the ordinary way but, on Monday, the fee to be charged had not been fixed.

Entering the main door facing Field Road, visitors were immediately struck by the light and airy atmosphere of the place. Single-bedded wards—which looked very charming and nicely furnished—benefit by a view across to Rodborough Common, while duty rooms, store rooms, bathrooms and the like, are on the less sunny side of the main corridor.

At the far end, facing towards Bowbridge, are the five-bedded wards. Into these the mothers will go for the last portion of their stay when they will undoubtedly be pleased to have a little social life.

Of great interest was the nursery with its rows of tiny cots waiting for the first babies to be born in this lovely place. To reach it one has to pass through a corridor built of glass bricks. There are no dark passages in this most modern of buildings.

Paintwork was spotless, floors were polished and metalwork gleamed as it should in a building said to be the most up-to-date of its kind in the country. The excellent state of its readiness spoke volumes for the work of the new matron, Miss I. Haskins, and her staff.

MATRON FROM TETBURY

Miss Haskins comes from the Cotswold Maternity Home at Tetbury where she went originally in 1937. Her appointment to Stroud—first reported in the "Stroud Journal"—is the source of great satisfaction. She has a staff of three sisters, three midwives, one part time midwife, two full-time ward orderlies and two part-time orderlies. There is also a porter.

Accommodation for the staff has been provided in Park Road, Stroud, a short distance from the new Hospital. In it each sister and midwife has a bed sitting room of her own and the accommodation for the other members of the staff is of a very high order.

Contrary to anticipation, no difficulty was experienced in obtaining staff, and this pleasing fact the secretary to the Gloucester, Stroud and the Forest Hospital Management Committee (Mr. C. J. Adams) attributed to the psychological effect of being able to work in entirely new surroundings.

Mr. Adams also said that although the Cotswold Maternity Home was now closed it was the intention of the Board to re-open as a hospital once more.

The new Hospital is described as the "modern pavilion type," everything being on one level, and there is special provision for ante-natal examinations.

All bookings will be made through the County Council's health service. Only where home conditions are inadequate for confinements or where there is likely to be some medical difficulty, will admission be recommended.

Mothers will be cared for by their own doctors but there will be consultants on call in case of emergency.

OPENING SPEECHES

Col. H. A. Guy, chairman of the Management Committee, presided over the large and representative gathering which assembled for the first part of the opening ceremony in the Trinity Rooms—conveniently situated on the opposite side of the road. He mentioned how sorry they were that it was Mr. Tanner's last public engagement in his capacity as chairman of the Regional Board, a position from which he has now resigned. He also introduced the new matron and wished her every success in the tasks which lay before her.

Mr. Tanner had a word of praise for the work of the area Management Committee and in particular for Col. H. B. Stokes (Bisley), the chairman and Dr. C. Cookson, the vice-chairman. He mentioned that Col. Stokes was also chairman of the Finance Committee and suggested that he took a leaf out of Nelson's book and turned a blind eye on the expense side of the new hospital! Other parts of the region did not find it easy to persuade him to do that.

In a brief review of the work of the Board which covers an area extending from the Scilly Islands to Tewkesbury, Mr. Tanner said it was the first time that a national service had been administered by local people in a purely voluntary character. The problem had been not to find men and women suitable to serve on the various boards and committees, but to select them from the large number available. That was a great tribute to the voluntary spirit which still obtained in this country and which prophets of gloom said that the National Health service would kill.

LONG OVERDUE

Mr. Tanner said the new Hospital was one of the few that their financial resources had enabled them to build since the Act was passed. It was a delight to see it provided in a district where it was long overdue. The new Hospital completed the Board's plans for maternity work in Gloucestershire.

Having said that the senior medical office was of the opinion that the effect on the mothers taken to the new hospital and the infants born there would be such as to make its erection a good investment and well worth while, Mr. Tanner remarked on the happy fact that they began with a full staff.

"I hope this hospital will prove a great boon to the inhabitants of the Stroud Valley and I wish happiness and prosperity to the matron, staff, doctors, to all who work there and to the patients there in the future" he said.

Dedicatory prayers were said by the Rev. E. H. Eynon.

GREAT DAY FOR STROUD

Mr. Mason described it as a great day for Stroud which had needed a maternity hospital for many years. Members of the Stroud Hospital Management Committee would recall how a site for such a hospital was purchased on premises adjacent to the General Hospital but that the scheme was never proceeded with because of lack of finance. Now the town was in the happy position of possessing a building of which it would be very proud.

In a chat with a "Journal" reporter, Mr. Adams said that the new Hospital grew out of plans originally drawn up by the County Council in 1947. Delays in completing the scheme were due to the change over of the National Health Service the following year, the allocation of money grants and the provision of accommodation for the new nurses. The aim had been to provide maternity facilities in the centre of the district from which the greatest demand came.

Ladies of Holy Trinity Church served tea to the guests after the opening ceremony.

The front page story in the Stroud Journal of the unit's opening

A NEW BEGINNING

THERE WAS great excitement when Stroud's new Maternity Hospital officially opened on Monday, March 30, 1953. The *Stroud Journal* was full of the
news that the 23-bed building had finally been delivered.

The decision to close the Cotswold Maternity Home in Tetbury and
build a replacement hospital in Stroud had been taken by the regional
board of the local health authority in 1947. Delays meant the new building
was not opened until just after the Tetbury home had closed.

Its matron, Miss Ida Haskins, had been appointed as the new matron at
Stroud where her staff consisted of three sisters, three midwives, one part-
time midwife, two full-time ward orderlies and a porter. The new hospital
boasted two five-bedded wards, one double ward, single rooms and two
private wards. Rows of tiny cots waited for the first babies in the nursery.

Admission was recommended only when home conditions were considered inadequate for confinement, or in the case of a medical difficulty,
and bookings were made through the county council's health service.

The following week the hospital was front page news once more as the
birth of the first baby, Elizabeth O'Callaghan, was announced.

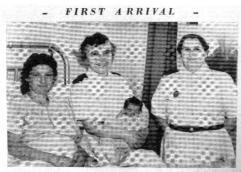

FIRST ARRIVAL

ELIZABETH, the daughter of Mr. and Mrs. O'Callaghan, of Cromhall, near Wotton-under-Edge, was not a day old when our photographer took this happy group. She has the distinction of being the first baby born at Stroud's new Maternity Hospital and she is seen peacefully sleeping in the arms of Staff Midwife Wright. With them is Sister Gleeson. To mark the occasion the Stroud Journal Ltd. presented Elizabeth's mother with a book of Savings stamps for her baby.

*The Stroud Journal celebrates
the hospital's first birth*

■ ■ ■ I was rushed in by ambulance, early on the morning of April 1, 1953. When I got to Stroud Maternity Hospital it was deserted and I was a bit concerned at first. My husband, Henry, was not with me because he was not allowed to go in the ambulance and we also had three children at home. But I soon had people in attendance and Elizabeth was born that day, at about 4pm. Midwife Ivy Wright delivered her. She was very nice.

Elizabeth had the cord around her neck and looked blue so I was worried. But they said: "Don't worry about the baby – we are more worried about you." I suppose I was so weak I couldn't move. I heard Elizabeth cry so I knew she was all right. They cleaned her up and wrapped her tightly and when they brought her to me I fed her straight away.

Because Elizabeth was the first baby born at SMH, I was given a book of savings stamps, £20 worth, which was a lot of money then. I was also presented with a silver spoon with her name engraved on it and, had we lived in Stroud, we'd also have had a new pram, but we were from Cromhall.

I think it was my community nurse, Sister Wheeler, who got me into SMH. It was the best of all the hospitals. I had six children altogether: Jenny and Kay were born in Chipping Sodbury, I had Raymond at a Clifton nursing home and Patrick and Michael in Southmead. Stroud was better because of the attention – the staff were always coming in to see if you wanted anything. It was very friendly and the food was as good as you could get. I wish I could have had them all there.

Even though Elizabeth was my fourth baby, I stayed in for about two weeks. That's what you did then and I enjoyed every minute of it. Henry did not come to see us until the second day. The husband of a Polish girl from Dursley, who had transferred to Stroud after having her baby in Gloucester, gave Henry a lift in and back again as we didn't have a car. They were very kind. When the newspaper photographer came to take pictures I didn't have any flowers, so the staff went round and collected the fruit and flowers from the other mums to put around me.

I remember Sister Gleeson, who was a big woman and used to tell me to eat loads of boiled beef. I think she was trying to fatten me up.

I didn't want to go home, but when the time came I went by ambulance and held Elizabeth all the way. It was only when I got home that I could look at her properly. The only times I handled her in the hospital were for feeding and she was always wrapped up tightly like a little mummy.

We were invited back in 1978 for the 25th anniversary fete, which I really enjoyed, and again in 2003 for the 50th celebration.

Rosalie O'Callaghan, the first mother to give birth at SMH

■ ■ ■ I still have the silver spoon with my name and date of birth on it. I used to dig the garden with it when I was little, until mum caught me! She passed the spoon on to me when I got married. When I went to school, my mum used to tell me that anyone born after noon on April 1 was not an April Fool, so I thought that my birth date was okay.

I will never forget being invited back to open the Slade and Trinity Fete, held on the Spring Bank Holiday, in May 1978, to mark the hospital's 25th anniversary. My husband, Jaafar, took me, my mum, my two sisters and our four children all over in one car! I had my daughter, Leila, on my lap for some of the photos. She was about nine months old at the time. We had a lovely day. They presented mum and me with a bouquet of flowers each and gave us tea and cakes and showed us around the hospital. They made it a very special day, at the end of which they said: "See you in 25 years."

Sure enough, I was back at the unit in June 2003, both for the 50th anniversary celebration and to visit my daughter, Leila. Things came full circle when Leila stayed in SMH for aftercare following the birth of her baby daughter, Rubia, in Gloucester. She had hoped to deliver in Stroud and was there a long time in labour – they were especially keen to keep her when they knew she was the daughter of the first baby born there! She said all the midwives were lovely. But she had to transfer to Gloucester Maternity in the end, for Rubia's birth on June 14. Within a few hours both mum and baby were back at Stroud, though.

*Rosalie O'Callaghan and
Elizabeth Shirwan-Begie
with the silver spoon*

Rosalie and Elizabeth at the hospital's 25th anniversary fete in 1978

Leila loved it in there and the staff gave her great confidence so she felt ready to go home after four nights. Later she said she wished she had stayed a bit longer. The care is second-to-none and we all recommend it very highly.

Elizabeth Shirwan-Begie, *the first baby born at SMH*

Leila and baby Rubia at SMH in June 2003

Elizabeth was the first of 415 babies born at Stroud Maternity Hospital in the first 12 months after it opened. Thousands have been born there since. There will be more about the babies later, but first …

1

THE STAFF

1 · THE MATRONS

Matron Haskins (1953-1961)

Matron Haskins with her poodle, Suzie

SHE WAS very strict. When she walked down the corridor with the doctor, you had to stop and let her pass. If she walked by and saw you doing nothing, it was hell. We always had to pretend to be doing something. Nobody was allowed out of bed when Dr Newton came round. They all had to sit up, with their beds made, looking pretty. He was the maternity doctor over all the staff and was very much respected. We used to joke he was the matron's fancy man because he never walked round with anyone else!

I had all three of my children at the hospital. I was spoilt rotten. When my first child was born I was really scared and Matron Haskins told me to come in at the first twinge as she knew my husband was on night duty. On the Monday night I had this little pain and went into the hospital. I didn't have the baby until Thursday, but Miss Haskins looked after me. She used to say: "My girl, don't worry." She made us work hard, but she was really nice as well.

Retired Nursing Auxiliary Teresa Lautieri

■ ■ ■ Matron Haskins was there when I had my first two children. She had a little black poodle with a red bow on its head which used to run around under the beds. You saw the dog before you saw the matron. She took it everywhere with her. Miss Haskins was always very smart and she got quite cross one morning with one lady who was sitting in bed with her curlers in.

Miss Haskins said: "I take great pains to look smart and presentable and I would be very grateful if you would afford me the courtesy of doing the same."

Nursing Auxiliary Maureen Tucker

■ ■ ■ My first son was born in Tetbury before Stroud opened and I had another five sons at home before having Diane in SMH. I called her Diane Joy because of the joy I felt at having a girl after six sons. I had her sister Janet in SMH too. It was absolutely amazing, a wonderful hospital.

Matron Haskins was very strict but fair. She was a gem and all the other nurses were too. I was in there a month because I had toxaemia, a form of blood poisoning, and she wouldn't let me go home. My husband used to come and ask when would I be allowed home, and she would say: "She can when I say she can." I had a ward to myself and was very spoilt.

Some of the mums used to go down to the toilets and smoke and she didn't like that. She also expected us to keep our lockers clean and tidy.

Elsie Brown, whose daughter Diane was born on August 30, 1953.
Diane, a member of the League of Friends, presented a commemorative silver
spoon to Isabel Billington, who was born on March 30, 2003, the hospital's
50th anniversary.

■ ■ ■ She had a suite in Park House. I think she had been an army nurse and was very military in her approach. You felt you had to jump to attention. I remember her getting cross with me because I wanted to live out in a bedsit. It was very restricting living in Park House. I had a boyfriend and I didn't want to live in.

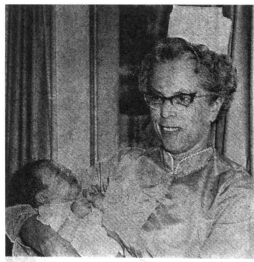

Miss Haskins pictured with one of her latest arrivals, Neil Henry
Mortimore, of Purton.

*Matron Haskins is pictured
with a baby on her retirement
in 1961*

She used to frighten me a little. When I was on lates I would wake up
hungry in the middle of the day and raid the cupboards, but she'd always
catch me.

Retired Nursery Nurse Ann Durn (formerly Jones)

Matron Light (1961-1983)

■ ■ ■ Marion became matron on August 1, 1961, following the retirement
of Miss Haskins.

She was responsible for all aspects of the administration of the
hospital, including seeing the cook each morning to plan the menu. There
was a large kitchen garden with two gardeners who would bring in fresh
vegetables daily.

Marion was very dedicated and well thought of, judging by the number
of cards and good wishes she received on her retirement. She officially
retired on December 21, 1983, her 60th birthday, but she was able to stay
until December 25 because she loved Christmas Day and all the
preparations.

I don't know what they did before Marion became matron at Stroud but she had previously worked at Gloucester City Maternity Hospital where a great deal was made of Christmas and decorations. She followed in that tradition.

On that last Christmas the usual procedure was followed with the choir from Holy Trinity Church singing carols in the morning, following a visit by the League of Friends who gave presents to each patient. The doctors, including Dr Hoyland, Dr Southgate and Dr Crouch arrived to carve the turkey and, together with Marion, they served the Christmas dinner.

Retirement came too soon for Marion and she left with very mixed feelings.

Frances Light, sister of Matron Marion Light, who died in October 1998.

■ ■ ■ Marion Light kept a strict eye on all of us. She had high standards, which she expected everyone to live up to. She also had a sense of humour. Mr Hamilton had great faith in her and trusted her judgement. I can hear him saying: "Over to you, Light." She was loved by us all and it was sad that she didn't live to enjoy a longer and well-earned retirement.

Dr Jim Hoyland

Matron Marion Light

Marion Light (left) having a drink with colleagues

■ ■ ■ In the bad winters, Miss Light would walk from Sheepscombe and still be at work for 7.30am. She was a bundle of energy and always running about. Laurie Lee was her cousin and he went to the hospital at Christmas with his guitar and entertained everyone.

She was a midwife as well as the administrator and she had an obsession with counting. There were some salad lettuces in the garden and she told us she had picked 56. She also used to tell us how many dandelion heads she would have to pick for her dandelion wine. She was very eccentric.

Retired Sister Freda Bishop (formerly Mitchell)

■ ■ ■ Both my daughters were born in SMH. Matron Light delivered Rebecca in October 1972 and Emma was born in August 1975.

Miss Light was ever so good and worked very hard. She would get a trolley in the morning and load it up with toilet rolls etc and wheel it along, cleaning the loos as she went.

Retired Midwife Esther Surridge (formerly Nimock)

■ ■ ■ There was no one else like Matron Light. She was very hands-on and even used to roll up her sleeves to clean the toilets.

She would count everything and she once asked if I liked gooseberries as she was going off to pick some. Later, she returned and handed over a bag, saying: "There are 36 gooseberries in there."

Nursing Auxiliary Maureen Tucker

■ ■ ■ She used to go round dusting everything, even when we were eating a meal. She once had a velvet dress which she wanted to wear for an evening out, so she hung it in the sterilising room and put the steriliser on full blast because she said the steam would iron out the creases.

She had these little whims. Debbie Harrison was the staff midwife at the time and Miss Light would only let Debbie empty the steriliser in the labour ward. It had to be cleaned out because of the lime and Debbie was the only one allowed near it.

We used to walk to Miss Light's sometimes and have some refreshments. She liked to have everything in order and all her flowers were in tidy rows. I was turning the car round once when I heard my colleagues shouting out: "Wendy!" But it was too late. I had knocked all the flowers down and Miss Light went mad!

Nursery Nurse Wendy Norman

■ ■ ■ Miss Light was not as regimental as Miss Haskins, but she was a very hard-working woman. For the hospital's 25th anniversary she made a stork out of papier maché and we all had to help break up the bits of paper.

At Christmas she made choirboys out of empty egg shells, bottles and crêpe paper and lined them up on one side of the short corridor joining the two longer ones. They all had little faces, frills and books. Decorating the

The choirboys made of egg shells

*Marion Light up on the roof
with the stork*

Christmas tree was her job. One year she did let someone else do it, but then she re-did it afterwards! We were allowed to decorate the Christmas cot and the nursery, but she didn't trust us to decorate the corridors and the wards.

We always went to a pantomime for Christmas and once we went by coach to Cardiff. We were supposed to take a large mince pie with us but had left it in the kitchen. We were sitting in the theatre when in came Miss Light, wearing her red and blue cape and clutching this mince pie. She had followed the coach all the way to Cardiff in her car. We couldn't stop laughing. She was an eccentric who had to look after everybody.

Retired Nursing Auxiliary Teresa Lautieri

She was as fit as a fiddle and hyperactive, always running errands and helping old people. Before she put up the Christmas decorations she would get a stepladder with a cloth and clean all the lights.

She climbed on the roof and put the stork up. But it wasn't up there long as the wind blew it down.

She had a little wooden ruler and went round measuring the tummies of new mothers to see if they had gone down.

Retired Nursery Nurse Else Gager

She was always on the go and would put her hand to anything, including gardening or cleaning. The hospital had a flat roof and the leaves used to gather on it, so she would climb a ladder and get on the roof to sweep them all up.

Retired Sister Mavis Cossham

Restructuring in the 1980s

■ ■ ■ During the 1970s, when the National Health Service was restructured under the Salmon Report, Joan Smale was the nursing officer responsible for the whole of Gloucestershire. She was based at Gloucester Maternity and oversaw Stroud and the Forest of Dean, which meant she oversaw Marion Light as well.

Marion Light (right) with Midwife Ruth Bell and the picture she painted of the matron's home for her retirement in 1983

The post of matron then became extinct and we were numbered. Joan Smale was Number 10 at the top, Marion Light was possibly seven or eight and was known as the nursing officer over Stroud, but we still called her matron. When Miss Light retired in December 1983, SMH came under the umbrella of Chris Crompton, who was in charge of the district. She was based at Stroud Health Centre in Beeches Green while I was in charge at SMH and was known as Sister Murrow.

The number of midwives had started to deplete considerably. It was quite a strain to keep SMH covered with enough staff. It was a tough time and that was one of the reasons why I took early retirement a year later in 1984, aged 56. Sister Mavis Cossham was then appointed to take over my role, with Chris Crompton still the nursing officer in charge overall.

Retired Sister Avril Murrow

■■■ I did the day-to-day running of the hospital although my grade didn't change. I was still a sister and Chris Crompton was my boss until Mrs Littlejohn became matron of Stroud General and also took overall responsibility for SMH. She stayed in post for about a year until 1988.

By then, there weren't so many midwives employed in the hospital and the community midwives used to come in to help out sometimes, but of course they were busy, too.

I left in 1989, and by this time Rosemary Radcliffe was appointed matron because the nursing officer title had been replaced again. We got a little bit fed up with the name changes, but we accepted it.

Retired Sister Mavis Cossham

Chris Crompton (centre left) shaking Freda Bishop's hand on her retirement. Mavis Cossham is pictured centre

■■■ It was a time when community and hospital midwives worked more closely together. It was the first time that a senior midwife had been responsible for the two strands of the profession. A scheme was started whereby community staff came into the hospital and hospital staff did sessions in the community.

While I was at SMH water births became popular. Initially mothers hired a pool, but eventually one was purchased and it is now freely available for women wanting it. In the Stroud area there were far more home deliveries than in any other part of the county and the midwives worked very closely with the local GPs.

My period as matron was the shortest I had worked anywhere but very fulfilling and a good lead-up to retirement, especially as I had started my professional life as a midwife. You never tire of seeing a new life come into the world and the joy it gives to the parents and families.

SMH was such a happy place to work but it was a continual battle to keep it open. It was a place where medical and midwifery staff worked well together and a very high standard of care was given.

It would be a tragedy if it were to close. I realise smaller units are expensive to run but, at a time when there is so much criticism of the NHS, they are a real oasis.

Rosemary Radcliffe, matron 1988-1990

Rosemary Radcliffe

Cecily Cook
head of midwifery, (1990-2000)

■ ■ ■ A traditional midwifery service with no doors on the labour rooms, peeling magnolia paint and a strong smell of boiled cabbage are the lasting impressions of my first day as head of midwifery at SMH in 1990.

I was given three objectives: change an £80,000 overspend into a position within budget, integrate the hospital and community midwifery services and improve the physical environment. By December 1992, with the help of the midwifery staff, I had achieved all three.

After 12 months completing the Advanced Diploma in Midwifery, I was full of enthusiasm when I arrived at SMH. I was slightly horrified to find that all babies were placed in the nursery at night and mothers were asked to walk there to feed them when they woke up. The rationale for this

Cecily Cook and baby Ellen

was to give the mothers a good night's sleep but it didn't give them the choice of keeping their babies with them at night or consider that the mother/baby relationship and feeding would be enhanced if the two were kept together. Separating a mother and baby would be unheard of today.

Being new to management I glibly announced that the practice had to stop and was amazed at the reaction I provoked. I was asked to attend a meeting with GP representatives from all the local practices and midwives who were not happy with my decision. After a long discussion we agreed mothers should have the choice as to whether their babies remained with them at night. I learned a salutary lesson that day of ensuring full discussion before issuing any alterations to practice.

One day I was standing in the midwives' office talking to one of the nursing auxiliaries when we noticed a strange man walking up and down the corridor, checking all the rooms. We challenged him in battleaxe fashion to tell us what he thought he was doing and he responded by asking about the visiting times. Having ensured he left the premises we were bemused at evening visiting to see he had returned, accompanying a woman. As Princess Anne's bodyguard, he obviously thought it safe for her to visit her member of staff who had delivered in the hospital, not least because of the two dragons barring the way to the ward!

When pregnant and expecting my first child, in January 1999, I had no hesitation in informing my midwife and husband that I would be booking for delivery in SMH.

Debbie Harrison was the perfect midwife to cope with the head of midwifery. She didn't bat an eyelid when I told her I wasn't considering pain relief. She just gently reminded me of all the women I'd cared for in labour who had needed pain relief and asked me to think about it.

I felt my first contraction at 2pm on January 18, 1999. By 6pm, I rang Debbie to warn her things were happening and at 7pm told her I needed to go in. I arrived at the hospital fully dilated and therefore did not need pain relief. I'm sure, however, that I caught a wry smile from Debbie when I said to my husband: "I didn't expect it to hurt this much," and he responded: "What did you expect? You're a midwife – what did you think all those other women were complaining about?"

I delivered Ellen at 8pm without requiring stitches and was in bed on the ward by 8.30pm. My stay in SMH lived up to all the positive accounts I'd heard from other women. The next morning several of the midwives came in to see me and offered congratulations, calling me a "jammy sod" as they left.

On the ward, what I enjoyed most was the camaraderie around the breakfast table, listening to the tales from other mothers and reassuring each other when our babies wouldn't feed or cried. I will also never forget the kindly words and hot chocolate offered by the night staff as they did their rounds and helped me settle Ellen. And yes, they even took her into the nursery for a few hours one night when I was at my wits' end and couldn't get her to settle despite constant feeding.

I left SMH on March 31, 2000, exactly 10 years to the day after I started. One of the midwives remarked that I had helped to bring the unit into the 20th century! With its future more secure it seemed a good time to hand over to Michelle Poole, who had the skills to take it into the 21st century.

Cecily Cook

2 · THE MIDWIVES

W E OFTEN USED to watch the sheep in the field where Weavers Croft is now. They were always popping out lambs and we would say they were in the right place to have their babies – it was the alternative labour ward. Like most staff at the time, I lived in what is now Park House. We had a lovely vegetable garden in the hospital grounds. Mr Wilkins used to look after it so that the hospital had fresh fruit and vegetables every day. Mrs Clutterbuck was the cook and she never wasted any food.

The consultant, Mr Hamilton, was lovely. We had a section for private patients and they were mainly his. Everyone knew him as Harry.

When I started at SMH, giving birth was a natural process. When people were having gas and air in labour, they would say all kinds of things and the men used to get very upset. I stressed at the antenatal class that they needn't worry about the swearing. But some of them used to get most uptight and think their wives meant it.

*Freda Bishop (front)
with colleagues in 1965*

I think there is too much choice now, too much information. One of the sisters came in with a man who was telling her what he wanted for his partner. She asked him when he had trained to be a midwife and he didn't say a word after that.

When I started there were 27 beds, but now there are just nine. Before the district nurses came in to deliver their babies, we used to deliver them all. At Christmas time, there was great excitement, the wards would be decorated and everyone could have a drop of sherry before meal time. They were lovely times.

Retired Sister Freda Bishop

■ ■ ■ When I started at the hospital we were very, very busy. There were often beds in the corridor, in the waiting room and in the office. Wherever we could put a bed, we put one.

Initially, booking for Stroud was made for social reasons – overcrowding at home and not having sufficient facilities for a home birth. If there were medical reasons or mums were unhappy about home deliveries and wanted their babies in SMH, the women were referred to the consultant.

SMH used to take mothers from quite a large area, including Tetbury and Wotton-under-Edge, and it was a popular choice. It was a GP-led unit and we catered for normal deliveries, but we did have quite a few twins as well because there were no scans in those days. One day a lady was brought in by ambulance. I looked at her and said: "It looks as if you're having twins." She replied: "Oh, don't say that, I've got an 18-year-old son and 16-year-old daughter and you're telling me I'm having twins!" The doctor had a look at her and wouldn't commit himself, but sure enough she had a boy and a girl, and she always blamed me for it!

For many years after I left, people would come up to me and say: "You delivered my baby", or: "This one's yours."

Retired Sister Avril Murrow

■ ■ ■ I really enjoyed my years as a midwife, despite the many changes we had to keep up with.

I did my general nursing training from 1958 at Stroud General. When I started at SMH, on April 1, 1965, there weren't general nurses, community midwives and health visitors – we did the lot.

I lived in the nurses' home, Park House, and we worked split shifts. The night staff used to wake us at 6am with a tray of tea and we went off duty at 9am for a full cooked breakfast.

Esther Surridge and colleagues outside SMH

I did my first delivery at SMH on April 4, 1965 and in my first year did 54 births. Quite a few private patients flew in from America. It was cheaper having babies here than it was there.

We took antenatals in for rest and did inductions, forceps – just about everything. We booked in Caesareans at the General and they would come back to SMH the same day. The staff used to play tennis on a court where the car park is now.

In those days women used to be shaved and it didn't half itch when it grew back. If mums were overdue we used to get them up at 6.30am and give them cod-liver oil, orange juice and later an enema to get them going in labour.

We used to have to wear silly little hats. They were part of the uniform and had to be worn at all times. If caught outside without a hat the matron didn't half tell us off. I was out one day when this old English sheepdog came up. As I bent down to stroke it, the dog suddenly jumped up, grabbed my hat and off it went with it in its mouth. I never did get it back.

A mother rang me one night at about 8pm and asked if I could take her baby from her for a short time. Her husband had died while she was pregnant with her second child and she was struggling after the birth.

My neighbour helped me collect the pram and all the baby bits and we returned with the child. When the baby cried at three o'clock in the morning I asked my husband, Phillip, to get the baby's bottle and warm it up. He said: "I've heard of people bringing their work home with them but this is ridiculous!" The mum was fine afterwards. I was invited to the Christening and we kept in touch for a long time.

Back in the 1960s the husbands never stayed but were called in when delivery was imminent. Around three o'clock one morning I gave the telephone number of one dad to the auxiliary. She rang it and said: "Your wife's just about to have the baby. Can you come in?" The man on the phone answered: "My wife's in bed beside me!" She had dialled the wrong number.

One Sunday morning I was making a home visit and saw that the curtains of this house were drawn. I knocked on the door to get them up when suddenly the curtains fell down and there was a man standing there, absolutely starkers. Apparently there was a wasp in the bedroom and he was trying to swat it!

Before water births became popular, one dad had built a big water pool inside his house. He had to cut the top off it to get it out. Parents could hire a portable pool for about £200 and I did the first water birth in the Stroud area at Cam.

I did quite a few home deliveries as well. After one lady had her ninth or 10th baby in this caravan, children suddenly appeared from nowhere and surrounded mum. I couldn't get near her. It would have made a lovely photograph.

I once went to book a pregnant woman with a group of travellers at Horsley. By the time I'd taken her details two or three others came running along the field saying they were expecting too.

On another occasion I went to see a lady who was separated from her husband and she asked if I would look after her children briefly as she needed to make a phone call. I fed and changed these two little kids and still the mum didn't come back. It was an hour later when she eventually reap-

Esther Surridge and daughter Emma

peared and said: "There was an awful queue for that phone box."

I was out one Saturday morning when the phone rang. My daughter, Emma, who was only about seven at the time, answered it. A lady asked her: "Can you get your mother to give me a ring because I think my waters have gone." Emma replied that if she thought her waters had gone why didn't she go into the kitchen, turn on the tap and find out! When the lady repeated that her waters had broken, Emma replied: "My mum's a midwife you know, not a plumber!"

Retired Midwife Esther Surridge

■ ■ ■ Esther Surridge, one of my fellow midwives, was not very keen on computers and when we got our new PCs she was reluctant to use them as she didn't know how to use the mouse. But everyone had to have training because the only way to put our bookings on to the computer was by using the mouse.

Esther was very nervous about it so I said: "Come on – I'll give you a quick demo." I took her into the office and explained she would need to lift and click to get into the next page. She said: "What with?" so I lifted up the mouse to show her and said: "With this." But she replied: "What – that? I can't use that rat thing."

Midwife Sandie Baker

■ ■ ■ Mothers were kept in their beds a lot longer then. They weren't allowed to get up until the third day after delivery. Then they got up and had a bath. They also stayed in a lot longer, usually 10 days. I think some mums go home a bit too early now and they are exhausted.

The staff included Mrs Adams, who was a brilliant cook and provided real home cooking, a Welsh cleaner, Mrs Davis, and Mrs Cremins, the seamstress, who made all the babies' nighties. During coffee breaks the staff used to make motifs for them.

Harry Hamilton, the consultant, would blow a fuse if a mum was overweight. We used to have a lot of patients come in for an antenatal rest. He would send them in to be put on a two-week fruit diet. We didn't agree with it. We used to have to keep them in for a fortnight and they were allowed 800 calories on a Saturday and Sunday before it was back to fruit on the Monday. They were frantic by the end of the fortnight, but they did lose weight.

We had a bazaar most years and we all made toys and baby things that the patients could buy. We had a social club which all the staff belonged to and we used to go hiking and on coach trips to theatres. When people came to work at SMH they used to stay for years. Even the domestics were there for a long time. If one of them left, word would get around and there would be a queue of people wanting the job.

Retired Sister Mavis Cossham

■ ■ ■ I started at SMH in April 1966. We were never allowed to call anyone by their Christian name. Patients were only ever known as Mrs so and so – even the single mums were called Mrs.

The friendship and camaraderie was one of the best things about SMH. Mrs Cremins made the baby gowns and they all wore the same. Midwife Kath Jones used to spend her breaks embroidering around the neck and on the front of the gowns. We had terry towelling nappies but no plastic pants, so these nightgowns were always tucked around the babies' waists to keep them dry. The babies were all wrapped very tightly. Security is one thing all babies like.

We used to have a wonderful time working on nights. When I first started there and lived in Park House we would wake up the day staff in the morning and say: "We could do with some rhubarb." There was a wonderful garden then and they would collect it on their way in.

There were canvas cots on stands which were all decorated at Christmas. When they got rid of the old canvas ones, midwife Esther Surridge had one which she used for her babies and I borrowed it for mine. They were very cosy.

When it got busy the 24 beds were stretched to three extra, with one classed 'in the doghouse'. It was right opposite as you went through the double doors into the ward.

Iris Smith

When they first brought in the 48-hour stays, all those mums had to go home by ambulance, escorted by a midwife. We went right up to the house and put the baby in the cot.

Before Weavers Croft was built we got foxes and cubs outside in the field, where sheep also grazed. My friend, midwife Maria Doctor was put on Harry Hamilton's diet of apples and oranges when she was expecting and she used to complain that all she could see were lamb chops walking round on four legs!

Joan Rachael, who now works in the hospital's hotel services, was on the same apple and orange diet when she was in SMH. One morning I asked what was on the breakfast trolley. When I found out it was sausages I stuck one on the end of a long knife and waved it through the door at her. I gave it to her in the end.

Retired Midwife Iris Smith

■ ■ ■ It was quite common when I was doing midwifery in the early 1970s to suppress the breast milk using drawsheets. You would strap the breasts up as tight as you could get them and it gave the mothers a lot of relief. The midwife would shave women before delivery so she could see better what was going on. Enemas were also common to start off labour and an episiotomy was routinely carried out on all first-time mothers, whether they needed it or not.

I came to SMH when Berkeley closed in 1988. So much has changed over the last 30 years, most of it for the better. At one time we used to inspect houses and make sure they were suitable for babies to go home to. Midwives would also hand-express any extra milk from mothers into a silver dish. Now we teach the mums to do it themselves.

Midwife Sue Eyles

Sue Eyles

■ ■ ■ The highlights of being a midwife in SMH have been working with the mums so we can go along with their wishes, having my own children there, and watching the hospital change over the years. With the gradual decline of GP involvement, it is now a totally midwife-led unit. When I first started there were a lot more staff and a lot more to do. Mums weren't allowed out of bed for three days after having a baby, so obviously we had to care for them and their babies separately. Now mothers come in, have their babies and can go home straight away.

When I first started we could call on the Flying Squad from Gloucester, but now, as a midwife-led unit, we have very strict criteria and there are a lot more transfers to the consultant unit.

We've always done home births and we all like doing them, although some places are less suitable than others. We've done them in teepees, caravans and in very smart houses with white carpets!

Many years ago we used to have private patients, who would sit in single rooms, and we would wait on them hand, foot and finger. These days we have single rooms, but no private patients.

I had two of my children at SMH, in 1976 and 1980. The overriding memory of being in labour with my first is that the Wimbledon final was on and the staff kept coming in at half-hourly intervals to tell me the score, which I wasn't terribly interested in. Marion Light delivered my second. I had a single room, private care and the staff smuggled in bottles of Guinness to help me breastfeed successfully.

The future is never secure but it's a wonderful place and I get a lot of calls from staff in other units in England and Ireland who want to come to see us.

Clinical Midwifery Manager Debbie Harrison

Debbie Harrison

■ ■ ■ I had to go into SMH when I was expecting my first child as I wasn't well. I had high blood pressure and had to be sedated. There was a field where Weavers Croft is now and I remember looking out and being concerned that the sheep were being rustled. The staff didn't believe me about the sheep and told me to get back into bed. But they were being rustled and the police had to sort it out.

When I started working at SMH, I was absolutely stunned by how old-fashioned it was. The mums were kept in bed until the third day. I did my training in Cheltenham and we were getting the mums up eight to 10 hours after delivery. One night duty I was in charge and matron asked me why I hadn't given Senna Tea to the mums to help open their bowels. I saw this jug of black stuff in the drugs cabinet, which looked like seaweed. I wasn't aware it was senna pods being soaked in water. I told matron that I had only read about such things in textbooks.

We were ever so busy. It was a 24-bed unit and we often had to put up extra beds because mothers were banging on the doors to have their babies in SMH. We also had private patients and I remember going into one who wanted to use the toilet. She was completely naked and when I asked her: "Aren't you going to put on your nightie?" she replied that she didn't wear them.

The staff were absolutely brilliant. We had a wonderful, thriving social club. We were always raising money and we knitted clothes for the babies at Christmas. The main thing I tried to get over to the mothers was to listen to their bodies. I usually encouraged them to get in the birthing pool when they were in pain, because it relaxed them and then they and I were in control.

I must have delivered seven or eight hundred babies during the time I was there. Each birth gave me such a kick. Nowadays it is so nice to have the dads helping and cutting the cord. One dad came in and warned me he was prone to fainting and I told him it was all right as long as he fainted towards the door. Some have gone right out. I've watched them go down very gracefully and slide under the bed.

One day, a lady arrived at the door in the final stages of labour, leaning against her husband. I pushed her to him, grabbed her legs and ran backwards all the way round to the ward and the baby's head was there. The only thing stopping it from being born was the tracksuit she was wearing!

She kept asking me: "What about your back?" The work over the years did take its toll and I had to have a serious back operation. I took early retirement in 1997 and for the first six months I didn't know what to do with myself. I missed it terribly.

Retired Midwife Maria Doctor

*Janet Hellewell was at the centre of the fun when SMH's "first class delivery"
entry won first prize at Stroud Show 2000 for the most amusing float. Head
of Midwifery Michelle Poole is pictured in sub-aqua gear*

■ ■ ■ Maria Doctor was retiring and I planned to give her a fitting send-
off after all the years she had worked here. Maria was ideal for a practical
joke as she sometimes got a little panicky. One night when she had me up
on call waiting for ages for one lady to deliver I decided what to do. I
thought: "What is the worst thing that could happen to a midwife on
nights?" And I knew the answer at once: to be on your own, in the car park
in the dark, with a breech birth! So that's what we devised.

Michelle Poole transformed me into a new age traveller complete with
black wig, dirty face with rings through ears, nose and eyebrows, and
tattoos on my bosom and arms. I wore an old coat with the lining hanging
out of the sleeves plus flesh-coloured tights with a hole in the crutch and
the foot of a baby doll sewn into place. I had tomato sauce smeared over the
doll and my thighs.

Michelle's friend's boyfriend, whom I had never met before or since,
played the part of my partner for the night. He really entered into the spirit
of things. We had instructed him to keep his finger on the doorbell so Maria
would come to the door in a panic.

The car was positioned so that when she came out of the main door, the first thing she would see was me getting out of the car, screaming. I got to the corner of the building, just before you get into the light, and screamed for Britain. There was a meeting going on in the Trinity Hall opposite and they came out to see what was happening.

My husband for the night had been instructed to keep badgering Maria so that she didn't have time to think. He was very good too. He just kept on shouting: "Do something. Don't just stand there!"

Maria kept trying to get me to go in but I carried on screaming, with my head down and pushing her away, keeping her at arms length. I didn't want her to recognise me and of course she wasn't looking at my face, so she didn't suspect a thing.

We kept this going for some minutes until I thought Maria was on the verge of keeling over with shock and that was when I whipped off the wig and said "Happy Retirement!"

She couldn't believe she'd been taken in so completely having worked with me more than 19 years! Afterwards I had to stay with her for at least half-an-hour, making cups of tea, until she had calmed down sufficiently to carry on with her shift.

Midwife Janet Hellewell

Stroud Show float 1976

■ ■ ■ I remember Andy, the publican of the Pelican in Stroud, when his son was born. He had just opened the Fleece that night and he'd had a few drinks. We don't usually tell the parents what they have got, we get them to tell us. When I asked him to tell his wife what they had, he said it was a baby.

On the night of the Millennium, we had a lot of contingency plans. There were four of us on call that night and we had to go to the hospital to see what would happen at midnight. We all went in with our partners. There was a woman in labour who had her baby at 11.50pm. We stayed around for midnight and I remember watching these wonderful fireworks over the valleys. It was a fantastic night.

Before we had our plumbed-in pool, we had a portable birthing pool which used a disposable liner made of thick plastic. I had a labouring mum using the pool who had to get out and walk around for a bit when her contractions had slowed down. I noticed that the pool was leaking and we didn't have another liner because it was the last one. Another midwife took over from me while I went home, got a puncture kit and mended the hole in time for the mother to get back in and have her baby.

I remember being called out to a home birth in a village near Stroud. The father had set ideas about what should happen during labour. He had read somewhere that women like to hang on to ropes when they give birth so he had hung this rope from the ceiling in their bedroom. However, she wanted to spend some time in the bath and was progressing quite quickly while he was asleep in the next room. When he got up she said she wanted the baby in the bathroom but he insisted she should use the rope in the bedroom. In the end we did what she wanted. I think using the rope was just his birth plan and, of course, women always have the right to change their mind.

Midwife Kath Lowrie

■ ■ ■ I got a full-time post at SMH in January 1990. I was desperate to have my second baby at Stroud and my midwife, Sally England, was on call for me for weeks.

In the end I was two weeks late and had be induced in Gloucester. Rosie was born on July 4, 1993, at 12.30am and I was back home by noon, which is something I now bitterly regret. I really wish I'd gone back to SMH afterwards.

Sally did the heel prick test, routinely done on every baby at six days old, and it detected hypothyroidism. I now use Rosie as an example to highlight the importance of the test to other mums. Hypothyroidism affects one child in every 4,000 and Rosie started taking thyroxine at 11 days old. I used to crush the tablets up and mix them with a bit of breast milk.

Rosie is now a perfectly healthy young girl.

Midwife Helen Conway

■■■ I'm from Berkeley and had both my children in Southmead Hospital but when I later went to SMH as a student midwife, I knew I wanted to work there. Once qualified, I had to get some experience elsewhere first because you start as an E grade midwife but need to be at least a G grade to work at SMH.

Many people don't realise you only get more experienced midwives employed at a unit like this, whereas larger units will have more of a mix.

I've been a midwife at SMH since 1998 and we each have our own caseload. I work out of the Chipping Surgery in Wotton-under-Edge. The women on my caseload mainly book for Bristol, but if everything is fine at around 34 weeks they can go to Stroud.

I also do a reasonable amount of home deliveries which are hard work but rewarding. I enjoy community midwifery but also love going into the unit at Stroud as it creates a great variety.

At larger, consultant hospitals you become reliant on other people. We don't have doctors around at the SMH, so you rely on your own midwifery skills which is wonderful.

Units like SMH are few and far between and are so valuable, a vital part of the community. Those women who want a more natural delivery should have that choice.

Four of us at Stroud have qualified in neonatal examinations. Myself, Caroline Saturley, Jo Morris and Deb Smith have all done the training which covers checks on the heart, lungs and other parts of the body. The purpose is to reassure parents as well as pick up any potential health problems such as congenital dislocation of the hips – 'clicky hips'. It's great for the unit and for home deliveries that midwives can now cover this role.

Midwife Bobbie Cullimore

■■■ I had both my babies at home and both were fast and straightforward deliveries, although the second was a bit too speedy for some.

My first baby, Charlie, was born in April 1995. I asked Helen Conway to go on call for me and I was in the bath when my husband, Gary, called her. At that stage I wanted to forget all about this home birth lark and have an epidural!

*Jo Morris, one of the four
midwives qualified in
neonatal examinations*

I was pushing when Helen arrived. She and Gary got me out of the bath and they called midwife Sue Hill, who got to us just in time for Charlie's birth. My doctor didn't quite make it. It took us all a bit by surprise.

Harriet's birth in March 1998 was even quicker. I was working at SMH by then and Helen was on call for me again. Michelle Poole, who lives just two doors away, was the second midwife. We called her at 3am and I think she would have made it in time if she hadn't got dressed! They arrived together to find the baby already in my arms.

I'd had a few contractions and decided to have a bath and then it had all happened very fast. I was cuddling Harriet when they arrived, so they emptied the bath and helped me get dry. In the end it was great, all very clean and tidy. Gary was a bit shocked but he now thinks water births are very straightforward!

Midwife Jo Morris

■ ■ ■ When I was in my mid-teens, my sister, who is 10 years older than me, was considering a career change and left a lot of midwifery material lying around and that was partly how I decided I wanted to be a midwife.

Esther Surridge, who was the midwife on duty with my mother when I was born at SMH in October 1972, became my colleague when I started working at the unit and I continued to work with her until she retired. When I had my daughter Madeline, in October 2001, I opted for a home birth in Tetbury. It would have seemed a bit strange giving birth at work but I could not have been in more capable hands as I had my Stroud colleague Janet Pollard and the Head of Midwifery Michelle Poole there.

After I returned from maternity leave there was a call from a woman who'd had her first baby in Stroud and then moved out of the area. When she had phoned her local hospital while in labour, she didn't like the sound of the place, so she called Stroud at 5am to ask if she could just turn up at the door. She promptly arrived and had a lovely birth six hours later in the pool. She stayed a couple of days and then travelled home.

Midwife Kate Adamson

■ ■ ■ I had an interesting experience with a home birth in Horsley soon after starting at SMH in 1995. When it looked like things were moving on, the lady decided to have a bath. It was a deep old-fashioned, free-standing bath which took ages to fill. When the water was deep enough I suddenly realised her partner had put Radox in and, because her waters had broken, we had to pull the plug and start again due to the risk of infection.

It took 20 minutes for the hot water tank to fill again and when she finally got in she was close to giving birth, almost up to her neck in water. There was no way I could lift her out by myself and her partner had gone to check that the second midwife was on her way.

I didn't want to deliver her in the water because I was on my own, so I pulled the plug, but the water wouldn't drain out. I called downstairs and her partner shouted back that I should turn the taps on in the sink. I was completely baffled and thought he'd misheard me, but after getting the same instruction again I turned the taps on in the sink, and lo and behold the bath started emptying! It was too late by then so she had a bath birth after all.

Mum was delighted but it was a hairy moment for me as a new community midwife.

I've always been pro natural childbirth and have been hugely impressed with Stroud. I don't think people quite realise what a service they've got. I previously worked as a sister in a Sheffield hospital which was far more hi-tech and interventional and Stroud was a huge and welcome change.

If you want a normal birth or a home delivery, SMH is the place for you. I think the potential pain is what scares people most, but if everything is normal you can cope with the pain. Not many of our transfers are for pain relief. Even if someone does have to transfer they will know they've done everything possible to achieve that goal of a normal delivery.

To get the same care as SMH from a private service would cost you thousands of pounds.

Midwife Janet Pollard

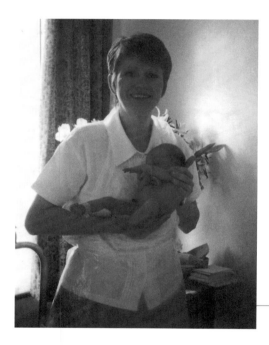

Janet Pollard

■ ■ ■ The day I gave birth to my first son Harry in SMH was the day I decided to become a midwife. I was exhausted and elated after an emergency forceps delivery performed by Dr Mark Porter. I remember very clearly being tucked into bed with my beautiful son and feeling so incredibly satisfied, so very special. I thought that if I could make just one woman feel as good as I did (sore perineum aside) then midwifery was where I wanted to be.

I didn't cast aside my journalism career immediately. I had been lucky enough to corner a good freelance market, writing for a range of women's weekly magazines and Sunday supplements. As long as I kept the ideas rolling in, the work was regular and varied, allowing me to work from home and be with Harry (I worked when he slept). Above all, the money was very good. So why rock the boat?

Yet that feeling simply wouldn't go away. At the time, and knowing what I know now, it was very idealistic, but it was strong, nonetheless. I can't remember when I broached the idea with my long-suffering partner, but I think it was fairly gradual. He has always been incredibly supportive but, like other members of my family, he wondered why I should want to swap a successful, flexible career I had worked very hard towards for shift work and the chance to earn a good deal less.

Financial considerations mean I have continued freelance writing throughout. I'll probably always write something because I still enjoy the buzz it gives me. Like midwifery, it is an art. As an art, however, midwifery wins hands down.

I still find myself grinning, both inwardly and outwardly, at the sight of a baby emerging from the womb, staring in wonder at the sheer cleverness of it all. I have had bad days but I have never regretted making the break.

Midwife Mandy Robotham

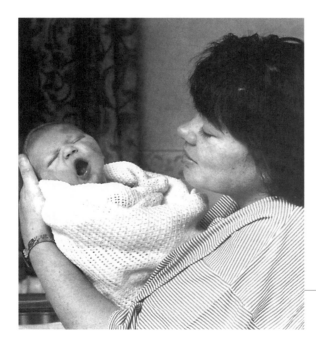

*Mandy Robotham
and baby Harry*

3 · DOCTORS' NOTES

S MH AND STROUD General Hospital both played a very important part in my 37 years in general practice in Painswick, from 1959 to 1996. They were a great attraction to doctors looking for somewhere to practise and I thought of them as extensions of my own practice.

I had worked with consultant gynaecologist Mr Harry Hamilton for a year, from 1957 to 1958, in the City Maternity Hospital at Gloucester and the General Hospital. The team consisted of a consultant, registrar and myself as senior house officer, so I gained an enormous experience in gynae-cology and midwifery. This was to stand me in very good stead and I built my practice around midwifery. It was marvellous, therefore, to have the use of SMH. I saw it as a compromise between home deliveries, of which there were quite a number, and complicated deliveries, which had to take place in the consultant unit at Gloucester.

Having worked for Mr Hamilton at Gloucester, it seemed natural for me to become his clinical assistant at Stroud in 1964. He came over to Stroud General on Thursday mornings and it was always busy. He started the morning with an operating list and then went downstairs to do his gynae clinic, leaving me to finish the list. I would then join him in the gynae clinic and he would go over to SMH to do an antenatal clinic. I would join him there and stay on to induce any women who needed to be started off in labour. I visited both hospitals most days.

SMH had a lot going for it and it had the facilities of the General Hospital very close at hand. In the early days we did one or two emergency Caesarean sections there. On one occasion I was called in from a game of cricket. Mr Hamilton lived in Painswick and was always happy to be called in. He was a very skilled and experienced surgeon.

Latterly, there has been a resuscitation trolley in the labour ward, which has been a very reassuring thing to have standing by. Most important of all, a midwife was always on duty, day and night. The midwives were the key to

Dr Jim Hoyland

the smooth running of the hospital and were a joy to work with. It was largely due to them that the hospital enjoyed such a high reputation and was so popular, as my wife can testify having had two of our own children there.

I count myself very fortunate to have had the opportunity to be a part of the team at SMH for so many years. I am left with many memories and in particular the sense of satisfaction felt when driving home, sometimes in the small hours, after a successful and sometimes difficult confinement.

Retired Doctor Jim Hoyland

■ ■ ■ On the retirement of Dr C N Royal, I succeeded to his single-handed practice and arrived in Stroud on December 27, 1962, at the beginning of an extremely severe winter. Two days later I was called to SMH to perform a forceps delivery on a patient whom I had not yet met. With my assistance she produced a boy 18 years after her previous baby.

In 1963, I was appointed as an anaesthetist at Stroud General together with on-call duties which involved covering emergencies and infant resuscitation at SMH, as well as Flying Squad calls for the hospital and home emergencies. Fortunately, as I lived in Stroud, I could reach the hospital in around four minutes.

On one occasion, with the Flying Squad present, we were faced with an emergency which culminated in the performing of a Caesarean section in the labour ward. Both mother and baby did extremely well.

As maternity services changed and mothers didn't stay so long in hospital, the number booked to have babies in SMH increased. At the same time district midwives became attached to practices. In my practice we were very fortunate to have outstanding attached midwives in Miss Thomas, Mrs Blacktin and Sally England. For a period in the 1970s, the GPs organised a rota system for nights and weekends. This sometimes created a heavy workload and my one outstanding memory is of performing three forceps deliveries in one night.

When I started to practise in Stroud we did not have disposable syringes and other equipment so everything had to be autoclaved or boiled for home births. Blood tests for foetal abnormalities developed in these years as did the introduction of ultrasound and foetal monitoring. Thanks to the League of Friends we were the first GP Community Unit to have such equipment installed.

There were many satisfying moments over those 30 years and even now I see three generations of a family I was involved with.

Retired Doctor Roy Lamb

*Dr Roy Lamb with his grandson,
Boris, who was born at SMH*

■ ■ ■ My husband Geoffrey and I have fond memories of SMH and my second and third daughters were born there.

Things rarely go to plan for doctors or nurses on the receiving end of medical care and, having had a long and difficult forceps delivery of our first baby in Gloucester, my consultant Harry Hamilton decided to induce my second baby three weeks early.

He knew I was keen to have the baby in Stroud, so when the surgical induction failed he proceeded to a medical induction, setting up a syntocinon drip. This procedure was not normally carried out in a hospital without resident obstetric staff. However, as we were both doctors, Mr Hamilton decided I should stay in Stroud and I found myself having to give instructions to the wonderful midwives between contractions. Geoffrey brought in a camp bed and slept by my side. Alison was eventually delivered by Mr Hamilton on August 9, 1964.

While expecting my third baby, Nicola, I opened the first family planning clinic in Stroud. At that time GPs played no part in the provision of contraceptive services, so our nurse, Rita Holland, used to go into SMH twice a week to ensure that all patients had any advice they wanted. Nicola was delivered by Miss Light in September 1966. This time Mr Hamilton was on holiday and Dr Hoyland induced me.

On his very first night on call after he arrived in Stroud in 1963, Geoffrey was called to a patient in SMH with a retained placenta. This turned out to be the rare "placenta increta" and he was obliged to call the Flying Squad from Gloucester. Along came a large, disgruntled Australian registrar complaining about "whingeing Pommy doctors out in the sticks". Two hours later he left a chastened man, pale and sweating, having struggled to remove the offending placenta piecemeal.

Other abiding memories are of the wonderful and very alcoholic Christmas parties that Miss Light and her staff would give in Park House, which was then the nurses' home.

Retired Doctor Rosemary Jones

■ ■ ■ Many of our night calls seemed to be either children falling out of bunk beds or midwifery cases. It was always good going to SMH where the expertise of the midwives made our job much easier. In fact, they did the work while we stood about doing useful things like holding the patient's hand or leg and shouting: "Shove!" Midwives do all the antenatal care and deliveries now, which is nice for the patients, but I feel that the GPs are losing out, and it's limiting the practical part of their medicine.

*Dr David Somervell and his late
wife Margaret*

The occasional rattling of forceps often restarted the uterine contractions and when that failed we sometimes had to resort to the forceps themselves. It was a challenge to know when to interfere, but we relied largely on the midwives. In those days the doctors did the sewing up of episiotomies and it had to be done carefully to ensure the mother didn't suffer afterwards.

It was exciting when there were two women in labour at the same time with the midwife running between them. It was one of our responsibilities to resuscitate the baby if it was a bit flat and not breathing well. This was done mainly by sucking out the mucus and gently flicking the bottom of its feet.

I liked dealing with mothers, some of whom were a bit anxious, and co-operating with the midwives, hopefully with a joyful and noisy result. Occasionally, we had to call upon the Flying Squad from Gloucester and they would come over with a registrar and an anaesthetist to do the needful.

I enjoyed the maternity part of my job. There was an end product, which was satisfying, and hopefully you ended up with a happy mother and father and therefore a happy doctor. When I retired, maternity was the thing I missed most. The great privilege of being a general practitioner was becoming almost part of the family and sharing their sorrows and joys and the greatest joy was the arrival of a healthy baby.

Retired Doctor David Somervell

■ ■ ■ I was house anaesthetist at Gloucestershire Royal from 1972-73 and I visited SMH on several occasions with the Flying Squad.

One lady remembers me sewing her up in SMH after an episiotomy to the sound of Bach! It was about 7am, on one of those sunny mornings when you are happy to be alive. I had been driving into the hospital, listening to Bach on the radio and when I got there I mentioned it. So we turned the radio on in the delivery room and I was stitching her up to Bach. She always associated the baby with that particular music.

Two of my four children were born in SMH, while the other two were born in Gloucester but came back to Stroud.

Our first delivery was done by Harry Hamilton himself, the senior consultant. My wife Anne had worked for him as a staff nurse on the gynaecology ward in Gloucester. He was a charming man and was always willing to help the local GPs. His plan was to start Anne in labour on the evening before his clinic in Stroud so that in the morning he would be able to deliver her. After rupturing her membranes, Harry said: "Now take your wife off for a gin in Stroud and come back in the morning." We did not even leave the building. Anne went into labour immediately and Harry had to come back that night. In the early hours of Valentine's Day, 1974, Jeremy was born. Anne was desperate to have her baby with her the whole time and eventually managed to persuade Miss Light to allow his cot to be with her in the daytime. At night, all babies had to be in the nursery.

My wife would say the delivery of our fourth and last child was by far the best. In the capable hands of Ann Hyett, our practice midwife, Emily was born in SMH at 5.45 on a sunny May morning to the sound of a blackbird singing outside.

Dr Ralph Stephenson

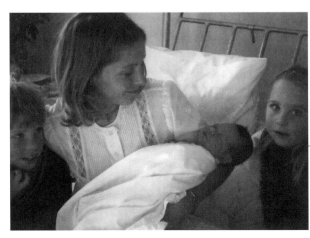

Anne Stephenson with children Jeremy, Charlotte and baby William at SMH in 1981

■ ■ ■ For two years I worked as an obstetrician on the Solomon Islands, at a unit which was in some ways very similar to Stroud. It was the main hospital for the islands and although the vast majority were normal deliveries, we did breech, ventouse, forceps and Caesareans if necessary. We were the main referral centre for the country.

There was just myself and one other doctor and we looked after 2,500 births a year – in Gloucester there are four consultants, umpteen doctors and other staff for 2,800 births. But it was a different world with a different outlook on life.

Before I joined the Stroud practice, in 1981, I came over to SMH as part of the Flying Squad for a lady with a retained placenta and third degree tear. I was doing obstetrics in Gloucester at the time. When there was an obstetrics complication, rather than move the woman, the Flying Squad would go to Stroud, Berkeley or wherever and deal with it. You had an obstetric registrar, anaesthetist and paediatrician if necessary. The only trouble was getting those people together. It often took longer than it would to get an ambulance over to Gloucester, which is what happens now if there are complications.

My very first call-out when I became a partner in Stroud in 1986 was to deliver a vaginal breech at the unit. She had got right near the end of labour so she could not be transferred to Gloucester. The baby was fine and she is still a patient of mine. I'd recently done a lot of vaginal breech deliveries so it wasn't too much of a problem.

Dr MacCallum's daughter born in the Solomon Islands with a midwife

SMH is a viable alternative to Gloucester as long as there are no complications. It's certainly a much more relaxed place to deliver than Gloucester.

I think the home birth rate would go up a bit if Stroud closed, but the unit should be there as it provides a service the other hospitals don't. If the health authority were to close Stroud it would not save much money.

I backed the campaign to save SMH because I felt women needed the choice. Neither Gloucester nor Cheltenham offer an alternative for those women who don't want a very hi-tech labour. There is always a risk, of course, and there is also the issue of some doctors who say they have become de-skilled in obstetrics. When they are looking at women having a baby in Stroud they feel exposed and don't feel prepared to take that responsibility. But it isn't the case now as the midwives are in charge.

A midwife-led unit can make things more difficult as we are now just called in for emergencies so we don't know the woman or her case history. But, if the midwives are taking responsibility for it, I don't see that as a problem and the majority of them are very experienced. The most important thing is that the health care system should provide the choice offered by SMH for women.

Dr Thornton MacCallum

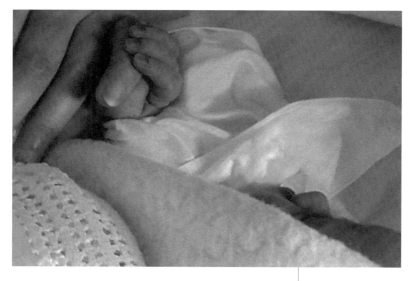

Photo by Jane Fisher

4 · TALES FROM THE NURSERY

I N THE EARLY days, the floor of the corridor was polished once a week. We had to vacuum and wash it with disinfectant every day and the porter would come along and polish it with a big machine. The hospital was kept absolutely spotless. We had to wheel all the beds to one side to clean the floors while the patients were still in them. Back then, patients had to spend the first four days after the birth in bed with bedpans and then, for the next three days, they had to use wheelchairs when they went to the loo.

At 7.30pm, we would go out into the corridors and shout "Baby time!" and all the fathers and visitors would go to the nursery. Then the babies would be held up at the windows because only staff were allowed inside the nursery. The premature baby room was a little room with a steriliser in it. We put that on to boil and it would heat the little room up because we didn't have incubators.

I was on night duty in 1959 when we lost a mum, who was a private patient. It was usual to wake the mothers up at 5am for their first cup of tea. We woke the mum up, but she looked really bad and said she didn't feel very good. I went back to get the sister in charge straight away, but when she went in the mother had died from a heart attack. She had been advised not to have the baby. It was a very sad story.

We had another patient who had her baby on the floor. She was in Room 6, which was the room where mums waiting to have their babies stayed. I went in to give her a cup of tea and she was standing by the bed with the baby at her feet. She had not called anybody for help. But the baby looked blue and I called out: "Matron! Matron!" She came and the baby survived and everything was fine. I was really young at the time and I was shaking and matron had to give me a cup of tea.

I miss the rapport we used to have with the mums. We helped them with everything and if they needed a sleep we would feed the babies for them. Nowadays, the mothers do a lot more for themselves. There was a great camaraderie among the staff. We worked very hard, but we all had a laugh and it was really enjoyable. We used to be at births with a midwife but new rules came in which dictated that two midwives had to be present at deliveries, so we weren't allowed in any more.

My first day at work was February 18, 1957. It was my first experience of England, having come over from Italy to stay with my brother. My sister-in-law was working at SMH and asked Matron Haskins if I could work there. She talked to me and I didn't understand a word. I thought I would be living with my brother but I had to live in the nursing home at Park House with the other staff. I was really quite upset. For the first week, I had another person to follow and I started by just handing out the tea. As my English improved, matron made me an auxiliary. It took me four years to get up to that position.

Retired Nursing Auxiliary Teresa Lautieri

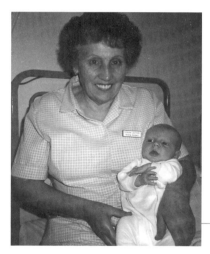

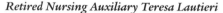

Teresa Lautieri and baby

■ ■ ■ Four of my six children were born in SMH. I spent five days in bed and didn't get to handle the baby until three or four days before going home. If you hadn't gone by 11am, you jolly well stayed in until the next day. It was very regimented but a lot of it was for the good of the mum.

They moved heaven and earth to get you to breastfeed. You certainly didn't feel comfortable if you bottle fed but breastfeeding was something I was never very good at. We had to sleep on our tummies, on a cushion, in the afternoons and were woken up at 3pm for bread and jam.

When I had my second child, Lynne, in SMH, my son Steven was only 18 months old. I didn't see him for two weeks as children were not allowed to visit. My husband, Eddie, used to bring him along Bowbridge Lane and hold him up so he could wave to me through the window. My next two were born at home and with my last two I had 48-hour discharges from SMH.

I was so pleased when Miss Light gave me a job as a nursing auxiliary in 1972. My first job was taking the flowers out at night. They always used to go out on a big trolley in the corridor.

The vicar, the Reverend Tucker, a big tall man who used to walk with a limp, came in to take a service on Sunday nights. They started at 8pm and I had to clear the flowers before he came in.

When the Flying Squad were called, they would come from Gloucester as a complete team with all their own equipment and trained staff. I hated it as I had to make tea for the lot of them.

Nursing Auxiliary Maureen Tucker

■ ■ ■ The trolley you see behind me is the famous baby trolley. We used to transport the babies from the nursery to their mums when they were due to feed. The babies were in the nursery at feeding time. Feed times were regimented at four-hourly intervals – 6am, 10am, 2pm, 6pm and 10pm.

We were always full to overflowing in the late 60s and early 70s. We were always laughing and often got told off for making a noise. One evening a mouse ran out from behind a wall. No one liked mice, so one of us put a saucepan lid on top of it and the lid then went off along the corridor!

Health Care Assistant Chris Mills

Chris Mills with the baby trolley, Christmas 1969

■ ■ ■ When I started at SMH in 1955, aged 19, the mothers were spoilt to bits. I used to show them how to bath their babies and I loved every bit of it. The nurses used to sparkle because we enjoyed our job so much. It was just magical. We never carried the babies anywhere. We had to use a trolley, even if it meant carrying just one baby on it. I can remember pushing the trolley once up to the main ward and glancing sideways to see one of the mothers washing her hair while her wig was sitting on the water jug.

I couldn't wait to get away on Saturday nights once my shift had finished at about 8pm. I used to tear off to a dance at the Sub Rooms to hear a live band. The fellas were among the main attractions of course. I loved the fun we had there.

Retired Nursery Nurse Ann Durn

■ ■ ■ I started work at SMH in 1956. They did everything then, including Caesareans. Quite often they used to wheel them across the road on a trolley to Stroud General. I remember a doctor doing the anaesthetics with a mask and ether for one forceps delivery in the labour ward.

Quite a few mums used to come from Tetbury. If they wanted to go home earlier than the 10 days we had to go with them. I sat and held the babies in the back of the ambulance and we had to carry them right into the house.

I went into labour while I was on duty and had a baby born at 28 weeks which died. Miss Haskins delivered it. It was a boy but I never saw him as you didn't in those days. All they said was that he had a birthmark but they didn't say where.

Joan Bruton, second from left, with colleagues

I stopped work in 1962 before the birth of the first of my two boys, Christopher. I had to go to Gloucester because I had low blood pressure but returned to SMH for post-natal care. I had my second, Robert, in SMH, delivered by Kath Jones.

I remember going to the home clinic run by midwives Joan West and Katie Thomas in Middle Street for antenatal checks. They lived and ran the clinic from there.

When I went back to work at SMH in 1974 there had already been many changes. I was glad when we got the plumbed-in birthing pool. With the plastic portable one we had to fill it from the sluice; humping those buckets backwards and forwards nearly did us in.

Retired Nursery Nurse Joan Bruton

■ ■ ■ I'd come over from Norway where I'd trained as a nursery nurse. That qualification was not accepted in England so I had to spend a year as an auxiliary. Miss Marion Light said that was wrong and she got me graded as a nursery nurse. She was very fair.

When I retired from SMH in 2001 so many policies had changed since I started there in 1963.

Years ago they used to say the babies should be on their side. If the baby was very unsettled we used to put it on its tummy for a while. Once settled, the baby was put back on its side. But now they must sleep on their back, with feet touching the bottom of the cot. The powers-that-be don't like baby being wrapped up tightly now either, but they used to be.

One woman was too far gone to be moved so they rigged up the labour ward and did a Caesarean there. It looked like a hospital theatre. We'd never seen anything like it with all the apparatus and tubes and machinery.

We had plastic bags full of sanitary towels. They would be rolled up and sent to Gloucester to be sterilised and, before cutbacks, we used to have 12 towels per patient per day.

There was some fun and games teaching new mums to put terry towelling nappies on, in kite shapes or triangles. Then, they would all be put in a bucket and left to soak.

I didn't speak much English when I arrived. I think a lot of people remembered me because of my accent. I often had the grandparents of newborns come and say I was there when they had their babies.

All my three were born in SMH. When my youngest, Tracey, was born in 1973 she was terribly jaundiced. I had an operation to be sterilised on the Friday in the general hospital and had to go back to SMH while she was taken for special baby care in Gloucester. She was Christened there because they didn't expect her to live. I knew she would be all right, though. There's nothing like a mother's instinct.

I was at the birth when my daughter Jacqueline's baby, Cameron, was born in SMH.

Retired Nursery Nurse Else Gager

■ ■ ■ In the middle of the night, at about midnight, we used to have to sit down to eat a three-course meal. The vegetables were served in silver dishes and we ate off nice china plates. It was like a restaurant. There would be four of us on duty and two of us would get the meal ready for the other two and then swap over. We would have a great banquet. It was a ritual I suppose and I remember feeling really full up afterwards. Nowadays it's a sandwich if you get time to eat it.

We used to grow vegetables in the garden and there were rows of rhubarb where the car park is now. It was like a little market garden. We had a social club and used to go out in the evenings or for an afternoon walk. It was a lovely atmosphere to work in.

Retired Nursery Nurse Wendy Norman

Wendy Norman (left) and Teresa Lautieri with baby

■ ■ ■ When the babies were ready for feeding we used to wheel them from the nursery to their mums on a trolley. It had rubber mattresses on it and each mattress had a baby's name on it. Eight babies would go down on it at a time. Once there was a baby which weighed in at about 14lbs. Every time I was on duty, I would find that this baby had been put right at the bottom of the trolley, so I would lift him up to the top which would make him easier to lift.

Once I remember doing my round at midnight and smelling Chinese food. It was all very quiet and then suddenly there was a burst of giggles. The mums confessed that their husbands had gone out and got them a Chinese meal and handed it to them through the open windows and they had all been sharing it!

Another time, someone in one of the side wards rang the buzzer. When I went in she was petrified and said a man had put his head through her window. We called the police and the next thing we knew we were swamped with police and sniffer dogs. They found footprints in all the gardens around the hospital so they knew somebody had been there. In the morning when I was off duty, I noticed that all around the General Hospital were Home For Sale signs. Apparently a few people who'd had a bit too much to drink had pulled the signs from gardens in London Road and planted them around the hospital.

When I helped with deliveries, I always felt sorry for the mums. The fathers would be able to see the head but the poor mums couldn't see anything. So I brought in a little mirror and they could see the head if they wanted to. On one occasion, the mother wanted to use it, but when I looked for the mirror, it wasn't there. The father said he had one in the car and asked if he could go and get it. He went off and the next thing I heard was a commotion and him staggering in with this full-size mirror on a stand, the sort you'd see in a bedroom! He stood it at the bottom of the bed and she certainly had a full-length view.

We had a lot of fainting fathers, mostly because it was so hot. There was one very big man with a bushy beard, who was wearing a mohair jumper. He got very hot and I told him he could take the jumper off if he wanted. Well, he peeled off and he didn't have a shirt on. He was very hairy.

My sister Sylvia had her baby, Sally, in Stroud while I was working in 1967. In those days if babies were born with clicky hips, they were put in a splint and you couldn't take the splint off as you had to keep the legs open. Sally's legs bent round like a doll's and I used to carry a photograph around with me of Sally aged two, when she was fully recovered, to reassure mums who had a baby with the same problem.

They were understandably upset and it used to ease their minds. Sally's now a professional dance instructor.

Retired Nursery Nurse June Strange

■ ■ ■ Matron Haskins was very much into discipline, but they all thought the world of her. My mum, Chris Anderson, worked as a nursery nurse at SMH where she was known as Andy. I remember going in to see her, particularly at Easter time. All the corridors were lined with tiny Easter eggs and little bunnies and were decorated with friezes of daffodils.

Mum used to tell me she didn't think it was at all proper for the men to be at the births – it was embarrassing for the nurses.

When I had my eldest daughter, Lisa, in Stroud in January 1967, mum was surprised I was allowed to carry my baby out to the ambulance to go home. In the early days matron insisted that the babies were put on a trolley and carried by staff from the door.

My mum took great pride in her job and loved it.

Jill Turk, daughter of Nursery Nurse Chris Anderson

■ ■ ■ My mother, Phyllis Cremins, worked as the seamstress for SMH from the time of its opening in 1953 for about 25 years. Her sewing room looked out towards the General Hospital and over the tennis court. Mum did all the sewing for the hospital. I don't think she actually made the uniforms for the staff but she did any alterations. She used to make and individually embroider all the gowns for the newborn babies and each gown had a different picture on it.

Phyllis Cremins (back) and Phyll Childs feeding sheep outside SMH

As a small child I was allowed to accompany mum to the hospital during school holidays. Sometimes, as a special treat, I was allowed to look at the babies through the nursery window. I especially remember the beautifully decorated cot that was prepared each year for the first baby born on Christmas Day. Something blue or pink was added to the cot when the baby's sex was known. As a Roman Catholic, mum was sometimes asked to stand in as a proxy godmother if any of the babies were not well and their parents wanted them baptised soon after the birth.

Miss Haskins, the first matron, used to wear a grey uniform and a starched cap. She was of the old school, firm but fair, and her faithful friend Suzie, her poodle, always followed her on her rounds.

I got the impression that the hospital was a very happy place to work and I know my mother enjoyed her years there very much.

Mary Hext, daughter of Seamstress Phyllis Cremins

■ ■ ■ Miss Light delivered my first baby, Kim, on Good Friday, 1964, and she's been good ever since! I have seen many changes since then and during more than 20 years working at SMH.

When I first started at the unit there were four of us on night duty. All babies came to the nursery at night-time for us to feed and care for. The policy then was that even breastfed babies had bottles during the night if they were hungry so that mums could sleep.

There were a lot more beds in the ward then and we used to have to turf the mums out to make the beds up before the day staff took over.

One day there were more mums with baby blues than usual. Nearly the whole ward seemed to be very tearful that morning. As they were so low,

Wendy Eldridge's baby, Kim

Nursing Auxiliary Maureen Tucker and I decided to cheer them up. I went into the old sluice room and found an old lampshade and some other bits. Maureen is quite small so I put my long duffel coat on her, back to front, and she had this lampshade on her head. We went down the ward together, all dressed up and singing *Underneath the Arches* in the style of Bud Flanagan and Chesney Allen. We had them in stitches. Then we realised one of the GPs was standing at the other end of the corridor watching. We felt so embarrassed but at least we cheered up the patients.

Health Care Assistant Wendy Eldridge

■ ■ ■ My mum, Sylvia Price, had me at SMH on December 15, 1955. She stayed in for two weeks and can still remember the doctor going in and carving the turkey. When my eldest daughter, Natalie, was born there in 1980 the first two things they did was shave me and give me an enema.

They didn't do that when I had Nicholas at SMH in 1986 and it would be unthinkable now. You were not informed about what was happening then and there were no parent-craft classes. You just went along with what you were told. I was determined to have Nicholas in Stroud and went 16 days overdue before he arrived.

I only stayed in SMH a couple of days with him, whereas with Natalie I had to stay in bed for that long! We were not even allowed to get off the bed or have a bath at first. We were given a blanket wash.

All the vases of flowers were taken out of the room every night and we just stayed in our nighties the whole time. All we had to take into hospital for the baby was a tablet of soap and a nappy pin. They were all put in little white hospital gowns. They looked like little orphans.

Nursery nurses dressed the baby to go home and they were always

*Julie Howe and family (above) and Midwife
Janet Hellewell with Julie's baby, Nicholas*

carried out by a member of staff to the car. Things had moved on tremendously when I got a job as a health care assistant at SMH in 1994 and they continue to change all the time.

Health Care Assistant Julie Howe

■ ■ ■ I was sick up until I was seven-and-a-half months pregnant with Michele. We lived at Butterrow and didn't have a car so I had to walk to SMH. I got told off on arrival because my blood pressure was up.

At one time they kept a check on your weight and if you were gaining too much they admitted you to hospital and put you on a diet. Some went on the apple and orange diet but I had a couple of lettuce leaves, half a tomato and a couple of pieces of cucumber. I think it was one Saturday night when my consultant, Mr Hamilton, came to see me. He was on his way out for a meal. He looked at my plate and said: "I'd sooner be having that than what I'm going to eat." So I pushed the plate towards him and said: "You are quite welcome to sit here and have it." It was ridiculous.

I was in a four-bedded ward, where the offices are now, and a lady in one of the beds opposite was on a diet too. We had to wee in a bucket, behind a curtain, so they could measure what we were drinking. I was in for three weeks and it was really monotonous in the end. I was let out on Christmas Eve and had to go home and do all the shopping. It was unbelievable. Things have changed no end, thank goodness.

Michele was born on April 28, 1967. I'd gone in the day before for my check-up and Mr Hamilton said: "You should have had this baby ages ago because you're fit to burst." According to him I was overdue and he broke my waters there and then and that was it. They had to let my other half know. Everything was packed at home ready. My husband wasn't at the birth, though, because it was not the done thing then. I had Michele at 3.30pm the following day. The three midwives in the delivery room – Sisters Bishop, Jones and Lovell – were wonderful. Sister Lovell, who was lovely, was in charge when I started work at SMH.

I stayed in for 10 days afterwards. You spent a few days in bed before you were even allowed to get up whereas nowadays some even walk from the delivery room. Back then there were no scans and you didn't have the classes you have today. There is much more information now. Ladies don't know how lucky they are.

Everything was very different by the time Michele had my granddaughter Victoria at SMH in 1986, just before I started working at the unit. I started as a domestic assistant on June 1, 1987 and my job title has since changed to hotel services assistant. There used to be four or five of us but it is now just myself and Brenda Parker who work as assistants in hotel services. There's a lot to do but we keep the standards as high as possible and we have always tried to have a bit of fun.

When Midwife Helen Conway started at SMH she used to ride a bicycle to work from her home in Rodborough. She had to cycle down Rodborough Hill and then all the way up to the hospital and we asked her why she did it. She always said she liked the ride in between! We could never understand that. We used to tie her bike up and put bows and sticking plasters on it together with little notes. She had to dismantle all our handiwork before she could ride home.

Hotel Services Assistant Barbara Portlock

■ ■ ■ I had both my children at SMH in 1971 and 1973 and I started work there in 1979.

Esther Nimock helped deliver my first child, Donna, and I stayed in for 10 days. It was a bit regimental but I didn't mind that. She was a forceps delivery, so they called Dr Mould in.

They only used to bring the babies in for feeding. On the sixth day you had to start making your own bed. They were high up and there was a little stool to step on to get into bed.

My doctor's midwife, Miss Rayner, delivered my second baby, Darren, and I went home the following day. If you were only going to be there 48 hours the GP's midwife delivered you. Going home so soon after the birth wasn't usual then, but I wanted to get back to my other one because she was only two.

I started work as a domestic assistant in what has now become hotel services. I was only going to work there a few months to get a bit of money, but I live just two minutes along the road and it fitted in. There used to be four of us but just two of us do all the cleaning and the food now and we seem to be on the go all the time.

I like the babies and I'm always interested to see them and find out their names.

Hotel Services Assistant Brenda Parker

Brenda Parker

5 · IN MEMORIAM

O N SEPTEMBER 27, 1998, a memorial garden was opened at SMH. It was dedicated to baby Rebecca Jade Hill who died in September, 1994, and nursing auxiliary Louise Holmes, who died in March, 1996.

Rebecca Jade Hill

■ ■ ■ I had Rebecca Jade a month early in Gloucester, just after midnight on September 25, 1994. I'd had pre-eclampsia and my blood pressure was high. We kept going backwards and forwards before they decided to induce me. She was a ventouse delivery but otherwise normal. I went back to SMH late that afternoon. They were very busy in Gloucester and said I could go back to SMH or go home. I chose to be pampered. I couldn't imagine having gone home and I am so pleased in retrospect that I didn't.

My husband, Keith, took me over in the car. Rebecca was feeding well and there seemed to be nothing wrong at all. She was perfect. I spent most of the night awake and watching her. Midwife Iris Smith and Nursing Assistant Wendy Eldridge kept a check on us. I was awake at 4am and Rebecca

Baby Rebecca Jade Hill with mum Sharon and dad Keith at Gloucester maternity

was feeding but then I must have dozed off. I remember waking up at about 4.15 and I knew something was not right as soon as I looked at her. She didn't seem to be breathing. I was still holding Rebecca and just called her name a few times to see if she would move, but she didn't so I ran up the corridor to find somebody.

I can't remember if it was Iris or Wendy who met me halfway down the corridor and took her from me and off into one of the delivery rooms. They tried to resuscitate her but they couldn't. Initially I panicked and thought I'd suffocated her.

They called in Dr Woods and he tried as well, but Rebecca had died. Keith came in too. Philip Ford, the funeral directors, took Rebecca down to Bristol, where an autopsy very quickly showed that she had definitely not suffocated.

We went home about 9am. It was very weird. She was our first baby and Keith and I had lived together in the house for a long time, but it just felt so empty. We went out a lot because we just couldn't stay in. I think it was the following day that we were told Rebecca had suffered a pulmonary haemorrhage which had flattened the lungs. They couldn't give any reason for it.

Professor Flemming in Bristol, who has done a lot of research into sudden infant death, said he had never seen a case like it before. He looked after me when I had Jack on February 20, 1996, at St Michael's in Bristol and again when Megan was born on May 27, 1998.

My antenatal care for Jack and Megan was divided between Professor Flemming and Stroud Midwife Sally England. I had four or five scans each

Baby Rebecca

time and endless blood tests, heart monitoring and other equipment. I was convinced it was going to happen again because they couldn't give me a reason for Rebecca's death. Then, after Jack was born, I thought maybe it was because Rebecca had been a girl. When I was expecting Megan I knew in my heart it was another girl and I was very worried. I remember being hysterical when she was born. I spent a week in Bristol after both births.

The memorial garden was Sally's idea. They were great in SMH. From the moment we arrived they were fantastic and they kept in touch afterwards. We just wanted to thank them. The garden was a lovely idea and we went to its opening on September 27th, two days after the second anniversary of Rebecca's birth.

I found it helped enormously to talk about her. Rebecca's death had quite an effect on everybody involved, not just our family but the staff at SMH as well. They were absolutely fantastic. Quite a few people had visited the day Rebecca was born in Gloucester so we have lots of nice photos. You reach a point where life has to go on but we will never forget her. Having Jack and Megan around is wonderful. We have always been open about Rebecca and they quite often talk about their elder sister.

Sharon Hill

Megan and Jack Hill

■ ■ ■ I was the person who put Rebecca into bed with her mum. It was just terrible. Sharon was very calm, she was wonderful really. Iris Smith took Rebecca off her and we tried resuscitation but it was no use. I then had to phone Rebecca's daddy while Iris was still trying to resuscitate Rebecca. I couldn't tell Keith on the hone, I just said there was a bit of a problem. It was awful. Sharon's GP, Dr Chris Woods, was on holiday but as soon as he heard what had happened he came in and stayed. He was wonderful.

We put Rebecca into a little cot. I can remember cuddling Sharon. I also remember worrying whether I had missed something. But it turned out there was nothing anybody could have done. Iris and I went to the inquest and that was heart-rending too.

Rebecca really was a beautiful baby. I'd worked in the special care unit with poorly babies. You accept that sometimes the babies are too ill to survive, but not when everything seems to be all right. It's a night Iris and I will never forget. We were all so excited when we knew Sharon had had another baby and everything was fine.

Nursing Assistant Wendy Eldridge

■ ■ ■ It was a terrible tragedy, the worst night of my career. Wendy Eldridge and I both felt so dreadfully helpless. We didn't know what to say to them. Sharon went home the following day and that was unimaginable – going home without a baby.

We didn't know what to do but just felt we had to do something, so we decided to send a bouquet of flowers with a single pink rose in the middle.

Midwife Iris Smith

■ ■ ■ I had a great deal of involvement with Sharon and Keith and they were a super couple. I think the saddest thing was that they never really found a cause for Rebecca's death. That can make things more difficult. It was a most terrible time, but one thing that did come out of it was a friend-ship.

I felt we ought to do something in Rebecca's memory and, with Louise having died as well, the garden seemed a fitting tribute.

Midwife Sally England

Sally England in the memorial garden with Health Care Assistant Pauline Lambert

Louise Holmes

■ ■ ■ Louise worked at SMH for more than 15 years as a nursing auxiliary. Before that, she worked at Standish Hospital for a couple of years, but had to give it up because of a bad back. She found lifting babies much easier.

Our youngest son, Paul, was born on June 9, 1965, a few months after we moved to Stroud from Kent. We had three children at hospital and three at home.

Louise took great pleasure in her job. I'm sure there must be a number of girls in the Stroud area named after her as she was well thought of. At least one couple we know named their children John and Louise after us. She used to help out a lot in her spare time with the floats for Stroud Show. She also designed a cot card for the hospital, which is still used, with a picture of a stork on it.

There was nothing bad to be said about her. The former head of midwifery, Cecily Cook, said at the funeral that Louise had always been a great help. Louise had retired at Christmas and from the time she was diagnosed with liver cancer to the day she died was just six weeks. It was indecently quick, but at the same time mercifully so.

We had just over two months of retirement together after bringing up six children. It was very hard. Louise had an awful lot to offer. She was a lovely person and idolised our children. I am just sorry she missed out on seeing our 10 grandchildren growing up. They are all so lovely. And, of course, our children have missed having mum around.

Husband John Holmes

Louise Holmes with three of her children, Maria, Helen and baby Paul

Louise (right) and SMH colleagues

■■■ Louise was great fun to work with. She was tall and fit and hard working and very kind to new mothers and staff. There was no drama that a cup of tea wouldn't cure. Over the many years we worked closely together we came to know each other's families like our own. She was always a great optimist and very forward-looking, moving easily with the times and changing practices.

Louise passed on the vast experience gained from having six children of her own and years of working with mothers and babies and her loss was deeply felt. It seemed very natural that part of the memorial garden was dedicated to one who loved so many. For a long time we took it in turns to keep it going and water the garden. It really is a lovely little area.

Midwife Janet Hellewell

■■■ Louise was lovely. She was a very good artist and went to art classes. Some of her work was displayed at the Subscription Rooms once and she brought a couple of the paintings into work. I said to her: "But Louise, you don't look that clever!" We used to have a real laugh together.

At Christmas we had a crib near the entrance and one of the nursing auxiliaries, Teresa Lautieri, normally arranged it. But one year Louise was doing it and she was charging around in a real flap. I asked her what was wrong and she said: "I can't find a virgin." I replied: "You don't get too many of them around here!"

Hotel Services Assistant Brenda Parker

■ ■ ■ She was a really good friend. I knew her before I worked at SMH. Our husbands used to work together and we went on outings with them to the theatre. We were all Londoners and had lots to talk about and our children were the same age. We got on really well and she had a great sense of humour. We also used to go to art lessons together, so we had a lot in common.

Nursery Nurse Wendy Norman

■ ■ ■ I came from Gloucester to work at SMH and Louise made the transition so much easier. She was a lovely person to work with. I remember her being very warm and welcoming, always with open arms.

Midwife Sandie Baker

■ ■ ■ Louise was someone I knew as a friend. She was always the same – a very happy person – calm and a good worker. She was just nice to know. She was very gifted and a beautiful painter. It was a huge loss when she died.

Retired Nursery Nurse June Strange

■ ■ ■ We worked together for about 15 years and Louise was a very good friend as well as a work colleague. She was lovely and had a nice sense of humour – always jolly. She was a very good artist and went to art school at Stroud College. I have one of her paintings. We missed her when she died. It was very sad.

Retired Nursing Auxiliary Teresa Lautieri

■ ■ ■ Louise was a warm, kind and very funny person. She was sorely missed when she died so tragically shortly after her retirement. We have a bench each in the the memorial garden for Louise and the baby who died. Louise was great fun and we always had a good laugh with her.

Clinical Midwifery Manager, Debbie Harrison

Louise in SMH

2

THE BABIES

6 · FAMOUS NAMES

E VERY TIME I pass Stroud Maternity Hospital I am always filled with a sense of pride at the fact that this was the place I arrived for real on this planet – 12.20am, August 15, 1963.

I don't remember precisely my first movements but I am sure that after a couple of slaps on the backside I was balling my head off, as you do! It was probably an early cry to have a bat and ball placed in my hands.

Many congratulations to all the staff that have done such a splendid job over the last 50 years. Here's to the next 50!

Jack Russell, MBE, the Gloucestershire and England wicketkeeper and acclaimed artist, born at SMH, 10 days premature, weighing just 4lb 15oz.

Jack Russell MBE

■ ■ ■ Jack's birth was rather quick. I was living at Wilber House at the Leazes and a neighbour took my husband and me to the hospital by car as we only had a motorbike at the time. I got there at 11.45 and he was born at 12.20am.

The matron was Miss Light, one of the old school, and she was lovely. It was wonderful in there. Jack was early and very tiny. I stayed in for about 11 days and we didn't have the babies by the beds then. We fed them, winded them and off they went to the nursery. As I recall the care in Stroud was wonderful and I had my second son, David, there too on August 4, 1965.

Our family doctor was Dr Halleden. He saw me for a check-up 10 days before Jack was born and said he would see me in SMH by the end of the week. I didn't believe him, but he said I was "ripe for picking".

As Jack was small, I had to wait for him to reach the target weight of 5lb before I was allowed home. On the 10th day he was still slightly under-weight and Miss Light informed me I would not be able to take him out. Dr Halleden came to see me and said I could stay another week. I was really upset and shocked by this.

He was a rose grower and always wore one in his lapel, so I told him that if he brought me a rose in every day I would stay. He turned, laughed and pointed a finger at me and said: "You wait and see!"

Later, Miss Light came back and handed me a red rose wrapped in a tissue. I took it home and pressed it when Jack reached his weight on the 11th day and I was allowed out to show him off to the family.

I think it would be a real shame if the hospital closed. I class it as a com-munity maternity home. They were so friendly in there. My grandchildren were born in Bristol. It would have been nice had they been born in Stroud. But my god-daughter was born in SMH. It was quite strange going back in to see her, walking up the same corridor again, but it was still as friendly and obliging.

Jack's mum Jenny Russell

■ ■ ■ The matron of the hospital at the time, Marion Light, was Laurie's cousin so it was all in the family. She was wonderful. You couldn't have a better midwife. She was very efficient.

I was 32 and considered old in those days to have a first baby. I think I stayed in Stroud almost a fortnight. Jessy weighed 7lb 2oz; just a nice weight, not too big. Laurie wasn't at the birth.

I have always loved the hospital. It is beautifully run and everyone I

know has been happy there. I have been inside the hospital since and it is still lovely. To even think of closing it down would be madness.
Kathy Lee, widow of world-famous author Laurie Lee, of Slad, who gave birth to their only child, Jessy, on September 30, 1963

Kathy and baby Jessy

■ ■ ■ My daughter, Betsy (known as Beano in my book *Love Forty*), reached her 18th birthday in February 2003, the year SMH celebrated its 50th anniversary. She was old enough to vote, get married, rent depraved videos and buy alcoholic drinks, but still not old enough to put her clothes away, folded, in the drawer, or deal with spiders in the bath.

My baby's old enough to have a baby of her own, though I'm hoping she'll wait a few more years before taking responsibility for another living being – bearing in mind what happened to the gerbil! If she ever does have a baby, I hope she finds herself in SMH. They would look after her better than anywhere else in the world.

When you're juggling with your first baby, you're more vulnerable, more desperately in need of support and reassurance, than at any other time in your life. Somehow, no matter how hard you try, you end up with the baby's right foot up your left nostril, the dirty nappy face down on the floor, and the clean nappy across the other side of the room or, even worse, missing altogether. And the fatigue! I know that long ago peasant women would give birth under a hedge and then go back to working in the fields. But for months after giving birth to my daughter I couldn't even summon up the energy to weed a window box sitting down. If Nature didn't cunningly programme new mothers to be completely besotted with their newborns, I'm sure some of us would escape from the adorable little tyrants as fast as we could crawl.

So, at such a tremendous, life-transforming moment in our lives, what we new mums need is understanding, support and reassurance. And that is where SMH comes up trumps. I still drive past the hospital sometimes and heave an affectionate, grateful sigh. I'll never forget arriving in Stroud from Gloucester Hospital, where I'd had an emergency Caesarean. I was exhausted, frazzled, starving, constipated, and completely lacking in the most basic of maternal skills. Within moments I was settled in a comfy bed in a bright, cheerful, and peaceful ward. A midwife spent ages with me, teaching me and my daughter how to breastfeed. Instinct isn't enough, sometimes – I've seen this, since, in the lambing shed. Fractious lambs and perverse babies need to be taught how to suck.

Only a small, intimate hospital, perhaps, could manage this kind of detailed personal attention. Large institutions seem, by contrast, to process their patients in an impersonal routine, and to have little or no time for anything but perfunctory essentials.

What's more, the changes of shift, and the constant variation of rotas, mean that in a large hospital, it's hard to develop a patient/nurse relationship. You exchange some friendly words, establish some kind of rapport,

*Sue Limb with baby
Betsy (above), and
together in 2003 (left)*

the nurse leaves the room and is never seen again.

At Stroud the food was simply marvellous – I remember the tomatoes were cut into decorative rosettes. Best of all was the divine peace and quiet at night, because the babies were kept in a room out of earshot of the sleeping mothers. It really did seem that I had arrived in Heaven without having to die first.

"We believe in mothering the mother," they explained, the angels. The only problem with SMH was having to leave it when I had run out of excuses to stay. I still remember the awful feeling of arriving home and realising that I had left the midwives and nurses behind. In fact, writing about it now, I think I'll forget that weekend break I was planning, to Paris or Amsterdam. I can't think of anything more wonderful, more relaxing, more life-enhancing than a weekend break in SMH. Nurse – the screens! A plate of salad! And a newborn babe to dandle for five minutes! And if, by some supreme stroke of luck, my daughter ever does become a new mother in the care of SMH, I hope they will have extended their sublime care regime to mothering the mother of the mother.

Author Sue Limb, whose daughter Betsy was born at SMH in March 1985

■ ■ ■ Moving house always makes me broody and it wasn't long after we moved to Stroud that I succumbed to the temptation of getting pregnant. Being pregnant in Stroud was very different from being pregnant in Wales, but I was comforted by the fact that my midwife was Welsh.

Third babies, they say, are always awkward, giving their mothers lots of false alarms, but when I woke in the middle of the night, I got my husband up and explained to my children and the friend who was detailed to stay with them that I was definitely in labour. In we went, into the warmth and cosiness of SMH, which was only minutes from our house.

My husband was on leave from the sea and the only slight disappointment was that my lovely midwife, Miss Thomas, was off duty. She'd been with me for every rehearsal, so to speak, and I was sad she couldn't be with me for the performance. Then the contractions stopped – they just went away. I was allowed out for a walk and my husband hauled me up the hill and down again, but to no avail. Fortunately, I'd been there long enough for my own midwife to come back on duty. It was Sunday morning. She said: "Go home, have some soup, have a sleep and see what happens."

If I had been in another hospital I might well have been put on a drip straight away and, although I was desperately disappointed to be going home without a baby, I knew I was lucky not to be strapped down by technology for another 12 hours or so. The following night, at about the same time, I was sure I was in labour but I wasn't taking any chances. I went downstairs, waking no one, timed the contractions and was comforted by my cat, who seemed to understand how lonely I felt. I really didn't want to wake my husband – he'd been up all the previous night – but eventually, I had to. "But I'm not leaving the house until I know I'm definitely in labour!" I insisted.

Desmond rang the midwife and she, lovely woman, called in to check. "Don't bother to get dressed," she said. "Just go straight in. I'll be there." It was very straightforward. My waters broke naturally (a bit of a surprise – they hadn't been allowed to do that before) and I didn't have an enema or an episiotomy. Best of all, I had a daughter.

Years later I was signing books in Stroud and a familiar face came up to me. "You won't remember me," she said. "I was your midwife." Later I put a very glamorous midwife into my book *Life Skills*. She was based on what I had learned about two midwives in Stroud who'd looked after my friend, Sam Adams.

Author Katie Fforde on the birth of her daughter Briony

Katie Fforde's daughter Briony and the cover of Life Skills

■ ■ ■ The two most important things in our life have come to us with the help of SMH, so it's no startling revelation that I hold it in high esteem.

It was probably because of our first born's diversion to Gloucester to be delivered, after 24 hours of encouragement in Stroud, that I gained a fuller appreciation of what SMH has that is unique.

The staff at Gloucester were tremendous and presented Connie to us safe and well, and made sure that mother and child could get back to

Stroud securely to start recovering. Everyone at SMH understands that time is a necessity, not a luxury, so parents can start learning to be parents.

Fintan arrived with less drama on a sunny Saturday lunchtime some four years later, but we were still glad of the reassurance and familiarity of SMH.

I think everyone who works there, and anyone who has been there, knows it is special. There are the extraordinary midwives, the touchingly considerate nursing assistants and the lovely Ovaltine and digestive biscuits. More power to their elbows and here's to the next 50 years.

Seán Gleeson, former EastEnders actor

Seán Gleeson with Fintan (left) and baby Connie (above)

■■■ My husband, Barrie Gavin, and I were new to the area and I did three things you shouldn't do all at once: give up a job, move house and have a baby. My GP, Dr Crouch, was very reassuring and soon put things into motion, booking me into SMH. I met the matron, Miss Light, and was thrilled to learn she was a cousin of Laurie Lee. I loved the atmosphere of a small local hospital, unlike the huge hospital I would have gone to, had I stayed in London.

My baby was expected on Labour Day, May 1, which seemed appropriate, but Labour Day came and went. On the fifth morning, Dr Crouch called by. "Maybe you should pop into hospital tomorrow for an examination," he said. "And by the way, why not take an overnight bag in case?"

The next morning, May 6, I climbed onto the bed for the examination and my waters broke immediately. I was not to leave for another 10 days.

Rohan Robert Gavin was born at about 11.30 that night, bellowing his entry like an opera singer.

Ten days later, I had learned from the dedicated nurses how to handle, bathe, feed and change my baby and we were collected by a proud father. It was the start of motherhood and I never felt happier in my life.

For my second child, I elected to have a home birth. I was reassured that, in the event of an emergency, I was close to Gloucester Maternity Hospital. I was allocated a Stroud midwife, who I could call at any time. The midwife arrived around midnight on the night I went into labour with a young trainee, excited to be at her first home birth. The baby was in no hurry until, at about 5am the following morning, everything speeded up and, once again, without the need for drugs, my daughter, Indra Helen was born on March 25, 1974. She was healthy, perfect and utterly beautiful.

I have always been thankful that both my children were born within their community, rather than being shunted off to the production line of a distant large hospital. It is an ideal to be fought for. May SMH and its wonderful services continue to be the first port of call for the people of Stroud.

Author Jamila Gavin, who opened the 50th anniversary fete in 2003

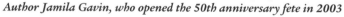

Jamila with son Rohan

7 · 1953 BABIES

I WAS BORN just after midnight on April 2, 1953, the second baby to be delivered at SMH. My late mother, Maureen Hughes, was staying with her mother in Chalford because my father, Alfred, was in the RAF. I was her first baby and she and dad were very young.

He was staying for the weekend with my mum at the time. Late in the evening of April 1 he and mum's brother ran down the road to the midwife's house to wake her up. She organised for the ambulance to take mum into hospital but dad was not allowed to travel with her as it was against regulations. He rang SMH the following morning, very excited, to find out what was happening. They told him: "Everything is okay. Your wife had a little girl."

My three brothers were born at home but mum went back into SMH to have her last baby, my sister Lesley, who arrived on May 16, 1963. I was 10 when she was born and remember welcoming mum home.

Jacqueline Hughes

Maureen Hughes and daughter Jacqueline

■ ■ ■ I didn't go in until the evening after Jacqueline was born because there were strict visiting hours. When I first saw her she was all pink and had not a hair on her body.

Maureen stayed in nearly two weeks, but only spent about five days in SMH with Lesley in 1963. She came home by ambulance with Lesley and I put our other four in the car and drove from where we lived in Eastington to meet them. We met the ambulance as it was coming round the war memorial roundabout in Eastington and then chased after it. Jacqueline carried Lesley up the drive to the house. It was a great time in all our lives.

Alfred Hughes

■ ■ ■ The hospital was very good and the nursing incredible. Shirley was the third baby born at SMH on April 3, 1953 and I had three more children at home. I went back to SMH 12 years later to have my son Matthew. It was wonderful. I used to think Shirley was the second baby born there because I was next to the bed where the lady got the silver spoon.

I felt very privileged to use the hospital. I am not sure why I was sent there because mothers who live in Tetbury these days all seem to go to Malmesbury and Shirley's children were all born in Wiltshire.

Patricia Morris

Patricia Morris and daughter Shirley

■ ■ ■ I was given three choices of hospital. Depending on the birth date, it would be Tetbury, Cheltenham or Stroud.

Sheila should have been born on March 22. If she had been, we would have missed out on Stroud altogether. But she was eventually born at SMH on April 13, 1953 and we were well looked after in the lovely new hospital. SMH and Stroud General do a wonderful job and it would be a shame if either ever had to close.

Beryl Ireland

■ ■ ■ An old school-friend of mine, Malvina Swain, and I were both pregnant and as SMH was nearly finished, we both tried to hang on to have our babies there. A month after it opened we were in SMH together, although not in the same ward as Malvina had complications when her son, Bryan, was born on May 1.

I lived just below the hospital, in Lower Street. When my waters broke, my husband Ivor walked me up the back lane to SMH. I had Susan about 7.30 the following morning, May 3.

We were encouraged to breastfeed and I never thought of putting my children on the bottle. We were always told to drink plenty of water to keep the milk flowing. One woman in there had terribly big breasts. Her milk had come in and I have never seen breasts like it. The nurses cut up a sheet which they wound tightly round them.

I've seen both sides of birth because I helped deliver my son Colin's baby when his wife, Christine, had a surprise arrival at home in 1982. It was an experience, but I was quite calm and when Matthew cried I knew everything was okay. The ambulance, midwife and doctor arrived later, and they cut the cord and took Christine and baby down to SMH where she was grateful to stay in a few days.

I loved SMH and have very happy memories of it.

Joan Rainey

■ ■ ■ I was frightened I'd have to go to Tetbury, which was much further away from our home in King's Stanley, so I was pleased when SMH opened and my daughter, Elaine, arrived on May 19.

It was strict, but I never heard anyone complain. We had to sleep every afternoon, even on the day we were leaving. Matron made me sit on the bed until the ambulance arrived so I wouldn't get tired. A few of us who were going out at the same time had been sat outside on the balcony, but she

Pauline Kuc and daughter Elaine

came on to the ward and made us sit on our beds and rest.

I was allowed out a day early, on the 13th day after Elaine was born, because it was the Queen's Coronation, so we could see it on the television. We didn't have a set at home but I went round to my neighbours. Before we left they wheeled a TV on to the ward for those staying in, so they could watch it the following day

As we left SMH, I remember the porter saying: "I'll see you all back here in a year's time." I said: "You won't see me," and he replied: "They all say that!" But it was more than 12 years later before I went back to have my son, Paul, who was born on September 23, 1965. Paul was born with two thumbs on his right hand, which was a bit upsetting at the time. He had to go to Frenchay to have an operation when he was a few months old.

Pauline Kuc

■ ■ ■ My first baby, Susan, was born at SMH in July. I had an induction with Mr Harry Hamilton, the consultant, because I was three weeks' overdue. You would never be allowed to go that long now.

He started to induce me about midday on the Thursday and I went into labour very slowly a few hours later. My daughter was born at 6.45am on the Monday morning. They wouldn't allow you to go on labouring that long now, either. It was pretty traumatic at the time and I had masses of stitches.

Sue Twiselton

She was a brow presentation. They turned her around and she was then face presentation, instead of the crown of the head, which is why it took so long. These days I would have had a Caesarean.

She was quickly taken away from me as she was quite distressed. My doctor arrived at about 9am and found me distressed also, as I hadn't seen Sue since she was born. He brought her to me before doing the required stitching.

It was a very pleasant stay afterwards. On the night she was born my husband arrived carrying a large suitcase. I couldn't make out why, until he opened it and revealed a huge bouquet which he had been too embarrassed to carry all the way up from town. How I laughed.

I was only 19 and very fit, the baby was doing well and I wanted to be home, so I think I only stayed in just over a week. We lived in Horns Road, just above the hospital, so I walked in and I walked out.

Peg Twiselton

■ ■ ■ My daughter Denise was born at SMH on July 17. I had to stay in for 14 days and had a nice rest while the baby got used to breastfeeding.

My second child, Geoffrey, was due on Christmas Day, 1956. He arrived early and I had special dispensation to go home on Christmas Eve.

I was 39 when I had my last baby, John, at SMH in 1961. He weighed 9lb 4oz, and arrived very quickly. When I went in nothing much was happening. My husband said he slept like a log because he didn't think I was going to have the baby that night, but I was induced and John was born in the night. When my husband came in the next day he didn't believe I'd had the baby until after he felt my stomach.

We lived in Bisley Road, so they walked down to see me. Children were not allowed into SMH to visit then, so they had to come round the side and I held the baby up to the window.

Betty Dobson

Betty Dobson and daughter Denise

■ ■ ■ I was in hospital a month with my first child Janet, who was born on July 31. I had toxaemia and there was a chance of pre-eclampsia, so I went in to be induced. The staff were very attentive. She was four weeks early and weighed just 4lb 6oz. She was very difficult to feed, so had to be fed by bottle. When I got home, it was still difficult so I had to feed her milk with an apostle spoon.

She was so tiny that clothes for newborn babies were too big, so my mum and friends knitted things for her. It was quite a worry to start with. My husband wasn't at the birth – he's not that type – but he was obviously worried because she was so small and he helped out a lot when we got home.

You never forget it when you lose a baby. I lost my son Keith at three-and-a-half months. I had him in SMH too.

But it's brilliant we've now had three generations born there. It's been lovely, especially seeing the first grandchild and great grandchild. I hope they never close it down. It's so convenient and there's more of a friendly attitude than in bigger hospitals.

Yvonne Smith

Margaret Wright and baby Pam

■ ■ ■ I went down to Stroud to see Mr Harry Hamilton, the consultant gynaecologist, one morning in September, three weeks before Pamela was due to be born. He told me the baby would have to be born early because I was very small. I returned to the hospital that afternoon, again on the bus, but had no means of telling my husband, Herbert, who was at work, as we didn't have a telephone.

The day I went into SMH I only weighed eight-and-a-half-stone. Many people didn't know I was expecting. They started to induce me straight away. In those days they gave you castor oil at about five in the morning. I think it was supposed to help with the birth. It was terrible to swallow and made no difference to me at all.

She was a breech baby and it was a very bad birth. My GP, Dr Crawford, was very good. He said: "No matter what time I am needed, I'll come." And he did. I had two doctors and two midwives. I think I slept for 24 hours afterwards! I was in for three weeks owing to the bad birth and they were ever so kind in there.

Margaret Wright

■ ■ ■ I had the second set of twins born at SMH, on November 6, 1953. There were no scans in those days and you had to be X-rayed to find out if you were expecting more than one.

I didn't know much about their birth. They were both breech and I was put under, I guess with ether because it smelt very strongly. I had a boy, named Victor after my husband, and a girl, Pauline. She suffered with

Victor and Pauline Shellard

multiple sclerosis for many years and sadly died in 2002. You never expect to outlive your children.

Victor was born first at 3pm and Pauline arrived 15 minutes later, with the aid of forceps. Both were a good weight. I'd had two girls already and had mentioned I'd hoped one of the twins would be a boy. When I was coming to, I remember the nurse shaking me gently and saying: "Mrs Shellard, you've got a boy." I was put in a single ward where I had the twins with me all the time. I was breastfeeding both twins when I left the hospital, which the staff were very pleased about. But I couldn't manage it when I got home, because of the older children.

Kathleen Shellard

■ ■ ■ From what my mother told me, November 20 was extremely foggy. My dad, John White, went off from their Thrupp cottage on his motorcycle to get the ambulance from the Stroud station. On arrival he was told by the attendant, Jim Bennett, that the other ambulance was out and he couldn't leave the station unattended. After what I'm sure was a heated discussion Jim agreed to follow my dad home to pick up my mother.

Once at the cottage they were greeted by my mother eating a large corned beef sandwich as she was afraid she could be hungry later. She and

Judy Dame held by mum, Lilian Jean, with dad, John, holding her sister Valerie

Jim then set off in the ambulance following my dad's bike towards the hospital. A few minutes later, dad looked behind and could not see or hear anything. Stopping, he realised the ambulance was not following and turned around to search the roads.

I am happy to say all 9lb of me arrived safely at SMH later that afternoon. My family and I now live in Ontario, just a few streets away from Jim Bennett and his family.

Judy Dame, of Georgetown, Canada

■ ■ ■ Our ambulance station was based along Lansdown. The ambulance service was manned by full-time paid staff in the day and volunteers at night. We would work from 6pm to 6am and on Saturdays and Sundays, all unpaid. Some men did it both full-time and as a volunteer but I was a tool-maker for Hoffmans.

Jim Bennett and son Paul in front of his 1950s ambulance

I once clocked up 72 hours in one week because we used to cover all sorts of things, like horse shows and the cinemas. They wouldn't have run unless the Red Cross ambulance service was present.

I remember taking Judy Dame's mother to SMH in 1953. One of the regulars had gone out in the ambulance with my partner so I was on my own when Mr White came in on his motorbike. One man could not go out with the big ambulance alone. There were smaller vehicles, but the volunteers were not allowed to look at them, let alone drive them. The dispatcher said I had to take the small one in the end and Mr White said to follow him home.

It was foggy and very difficult to work the gears, which were different to the big ambulance, and I lost him straight away. When I arrived, Mrs White was out in the street, eating a corned beef sandwich. I remember laying a rubber sheet on the seat and putting her in the vehicle, and off we went to the hospital. We moved to Canada in 1957 and I now live near Judy in Georgetown.

Jim Bennett, former Red Cross ambulance volunteer

■ ■ ■ I had my first baby in Dudbridge Nursing Home and wasn't very happy there. When my son, Stuart, was born at SMH, on December 13, 1953, it was a totally different experience. They treated me marvellously. His birth was very straightforward, apart from a bit of jaundice. It was a bit of a rush job though – I left it until the last minute to go in because of my daughter Gillian. We lived in Thrupp and I was taken in by ambulance at about 2am. My husband, Eric, went with me. They took me straight in and he walked back home. Stuart was born within half an hour of my arrival and before Eric got home.

I was determined to be home for Christmas because of Gillian and I got there. They let me out on Christmas Eve and we had a lovely time.

Before I left, the choir came round singing carols and Stuart was the only one who cried all the way through. He had a very high pitched cry and I always knew it was feeding time because I could hear him. He was always brought to me first!

Joan Bliss

8 · CHRISTMAS

SMH STAFF have always made Christmas special. In the early 1950s, Christmas Day babies used to be put in a decorated crib and on every cot there was a stocking with presents for mother and child – usually made by staff.

It was the matron's job to decorate the tree and her enthusiasm to create a festive atmosphere was infectious.

■ ■ ■ I spent Christmas in the hospital because you stayed in for 10 days then. I've still got the little card they put on the end of the cot. I was in hospital at the same time as another mother whose surname was Christmas. I had never been in a hospital before and husbands were not allowed in, so I was quite on my own.

The treatment was very good. My doctor was present at the birth and came to see me a couple of times. In the afternoons we had to sleep on our stomachs. I think it helped our wombs settle down. My husband didn't see Ian until the day after his birth on December 18, 1953. He wanted to call him Oscar and he did for quite a while. But I thought it was a dreadful name!

Margaret Hamilton

■ ■ ■ I was in labour more or less all day and my mother called for an ambulance at 6.30pm on December 23, 1953. On the way the driver asked if it would be all right if he stopped off and picked up a watch from the watch mender. He got me to the hospital but within 15 minutes it was all over and Dennis was born. If he'd been any longer collecting his watch, I would have had my son in the ambulance.

My brother and husband were in the army. When Dennis was born, my mother sent a telegram to my husband who was given leave to come and see me. But when he arrived on Christmas Eve, my brother was already at my bedside, in uniform. As my husband started walking into the ward he was stopped by the matron, who wouldn't let him in. She told him there was already a soldier with me. He wasn't very happy and said something like: "Kick him out!" before realising it was my brother. They did, however, give him an extra half-an-hour's visiting time because he had arrived late.

They also asked if he wanted Christmas dinner with me, but he had too much to drink and arrived too late! I didn't mind though; I really enjoyed myself. I loved my Christmas there. The doctor came to cut the turkey and we had a proper Christmas lunch. A choir came and woke us up by singing around the Christmas tree. It was absolutely fantastic. It was a beautiful hospital and it still is.

Pauline Brown

Dennis Brown

■ ■ ■ Christmas was a big, big thing. My children would come in, be shown round and be allowed to peep at the babies and matron would always have a present for them on the tree. Those of us on nights on Christmas Eve would put little stockings on every cot and a present for the mother on the bed.

On Christmas morning, the mums would still be woken up at 6am for swabbing. When I first started at Stroud, there was a sister who wanted us to sing carols on Christmas morning, so the four of us would dress up in capes and wake the mums up singing carols. One year, this sister decided that instead of singing she would bring in a wind-up gramophone which we put on a trolley. It was my job to switch the record on. I remember pushing this thing through the double doors and switching it on, but what I didn't realise was that it was on double or treble speed. I'll never forget *Christians Awake, Salute the Happy Morn* sounding like Pinky and Perky and seeing all the mums shoot out of bed with their curlers in. The sister looked at me. She wasn't amused, but then the mums all started to laugh and we doubled up. I was teased about that for a long time.

Nursery Nurse June Strange (formerly Gazzard)

June Strange with a Christmas baby

■ ■ ■ Dr Newton was a first-class doctor, but he always seemed to have a very long face. He had a soft spot for Matron Haskins and I remember he was given this ridiculous chef's hat to wear at Christmas as he carved the turkey.

On Christmas Eve, we had turned our capes inside out and walked down the long corridor to the main ward holding a candle. One time I remember one of the nurses crying as we did so. She was Roman Catholic and wanted to marry someone who wasn't and her parents wouldn't let them. She was very upset. I guess the singing made her quite emotional. I felt so sorry for her.

Nursery Nurse Ann Durn (formerly Jones)

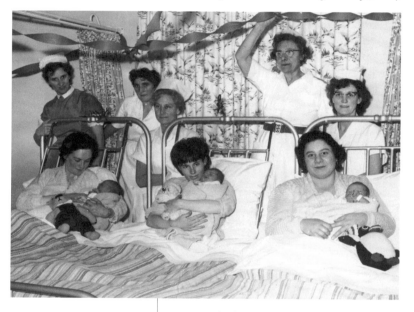

Matron Light (back, left) celebrates Christmas 1961 with staff and mums

■ ■ ■ We used to have a crib which was all trimmed up with lace at Christmas, with its own hood. The League of Friends gave a silver spoon to any baby born on Christmas Day and we made the babies a garment or toy to put in their Christmas stockings. This was usually done during our coffee breaks. Dr Crouch used to carve the turkey and give the mums a drink.

The choir from Trinity Church came round and had mince pies afterwards. The Christmas lunch was made by Mrs Adams, who was a brilliant cook. It was real home cooking. Marvellous.

Sister Mavis Cossham (formerly Lovell)

Holy Trinity Church
choristers singing carols in
the hospital

■ ■ ■ Two of my three children were delivered at SMH. Katrina, our first, born in 1969, resulted in a stay of nine days. For Victoria, born in 1972, I stayed just two days.

Katrina arrived on December 17, which meant Christmas in hospital, although this was reduced by a day when, as a Yuletide concession, the authorities allowed me home early.

That first stay at SMH was a memorable, magical experience. Looking back, I realise much of this was due to the atmosphere within the hospital. On the days approaching Christmas Day I watched as the matron, Miss Light, balanced on a stepladder and dusted beams before draping the decorations over them.

There were carol singers on Christmas Eve and Christmas Day, and staff sang us awake in the darkness of Christmas morning with candles and presents, many of which they had made themselves. Those of us who were allowed up ate Christmas lunch at long trestle-tables and the meal was presided over by doctors in fancy hats, one of whom carved the turkey. There was even a glass of wine. In the afternoon, a special Christmas tea was served to mums and visitors alike. The mum in the bed next to me had no visitors, so staff shared this time with her to make sure she was not left out.

Boxing Day morning brought its own excitement because I was going home. Before I departed, the League of Friends arrived with presents for the babies and mums. Katrina received a miniature blue Wedgwood cup and saucer and I got some toiletries. A vivid memory of this first visit was the babies mewing like kittens as they were wheeled into the ward in their blue and white shawls on long trolleys.

The delivery of Victoria two years later was different for several reasons. It was shorter and less social, because of my installation in a one-bedded side ward. Following admission and a speedy birth, the Flying Squad of medical staff from Gloucester was summoned in the early hours to remove a retained placenta. Their slightly green pallor following a breakneck journey summed up the urgency of the occasion. Baby three, Kevin, was delivered in Gloucester. Although kindness and efficiency prevailed as before, at Gloucester there was none of the tranquillity of SMH where babies were fed on demand and cots were in the ward by beds.

Joy Thacker

Line drawing of a baby trolley by Jacquie Govier

9 · THROUGH THE DECADES

The 1950s

I N THE 1950S SMH had some very strict rules and was presided over by the matron, Miss Light, who insisted these were followed. No family members were allowed at the birth and, if I remember correctly, only fathers could visit. Babies were kept in the nursery, except for feeding times when they were pushed into the ward on a two-tier trolley, all tightly cocooned like mummies. If you were caught unwrapping them, then woe betide you!

On about the 10th day after the birth of my first baby, Helen, I remember being unable to resist the temptation to take a quick peep to check she had the correct number of fingers and toes. As I started to gently lift the cover from the tightly-wound baby, I was spotted by the ward sister and severely reprimanded and threatened with the wrath of matron.

Fathers were only given a brief glimpse of their babies during visiting. This consisted of a nurse holding the child up inside the nursery and the parent peering through the glass. So the first contact with their child was when the baby was brought home. Mothers were required to stay in hospital for 12 to 14 days. How much more relaxed things are today!

My second child was born at seven minutes to seven on the seventh day of the seventh month on a Sunday, in 1957, after quite a difficult birth. As a result I was placed in a side ward to recover and not shown my baby.

The following morning a very frustrated nurse hurried into the room with a crying baby, and anxiously inquired: "What did you have?" Odd question I thought: I had a baby! When I gathered she meant what sex, I said: "A boy." Pushing the baby forward, she said: "Is this yours? It must be

Helen and baby
Malcolm Strang

because he's the only one who hasn't been fed."

As I hadn't seen my baby before, how could I be sure? But he bore resemblances to other members of my family, so I was convinced he belonged to me. The confusion arose because he wasn't wearing an identity band, so hopefully I didn't spend the following years nurturing someone else's child. In truth, I'm 100 per cent positive he is mine because he inherited my worst habit: always being late.

I'd decided to name him Malcolm Keith so was furious when one of the other mothers pointed out the birth announcements in the paper. My husband had called him Malcolm James, after himself.

When I had my third child, Berni, in 1960 I remember an Italian cleaner hoovering around my feet and whistling away while I was having contractions.

Depending on how long you had been in, you gradually got moved down the corridor, nearer to the door. You always knew the one in the bed nearest the door was the next to go home.

It is so much more relaxed in Stroud nowadays. It's an incredible place, a fantastic hospital, and it would be such a shame if it closed.

Malvina Strang

■ ■ ■ We were living in a small cottage in Leonard Stanley, Richard was my first child and I was determined to have him in hospital. We had no bathrooms at home, just a geyser over the sink. But the district nurse for the village preferred to deliver babies at home – it was normal then – and I was told I didn't qualify to be admitted. The only way I could get into SMH was to pay. I have still got the bill, for 12 days from April 7, 1956. It was two

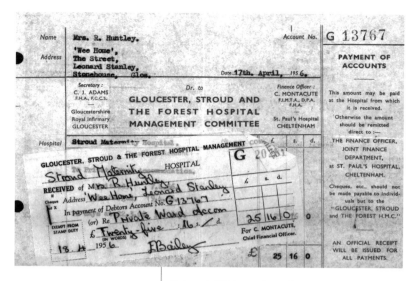

Roberta's bill for staying at SMH as a private patient

pounds, three shillings per day, so the bill came to 25 pounds 16 shillings.

The matron, Miss Haskins, always had a little black poodle trailing after her. I told her we could only just manage to pay and if anything went wrong we would struggle. But she reassured us and said not to worry, they would sort it out.

My husband, Laurie, was working in the local factory. He couldn't afford to be at home like dads today. He came in to see our son for the first time after he had finished night work. There wasn't any question of husbands coming in for the birth then. As a private patient I could have visitors at any time, while visiting times for other mums were restricted. I also had my food served to my bedside, on a silver-plated tray.

I had my daughter, Nicola, in 1959 and everything had changed by then. I had no trouble getting into the hospital, there was no bill to pay and I was in the ward with everybody else. The nurses were all wonderful and I thought the matron was very efficient and kind.

Roberta Huntley

■ ■ ■ When my husband came to see Susan, who was born in April, 1957, he was shown a baby with black hair and, as both of us were fair, realised they had placed the wrong child in the cot.

I was in hospital for six weeks and my daughter had to go into isolation. We didn't know what the matter was. I didn't see her for a week as she was in the isolation hospital at Over. When we did eventually bring her home, we checked to make sure we had the right baby. We always have a laugh about it.

June Ball

■ ■ ■ My husband saw me on to the ward, said goodbye and went. No husbands stopped then. He had to ring up to find out if I'd had the baby and he came in the next night. Because we didn't have a car, my mother picked him up.

When he came to visit me after Kim was born on February 24, 1959, the baby wasn't with me. He asked where he was and one of the mums said: "Dads don't see the babies tonight – it's only every other night." But the nurse took him to the nursery anyway. He didn't realise he was supposed to stay in the corridor and instead followed the nurse in to the cot side.

The next night, the official night for the dads, he went with all the other fathers and, like them, was only allowed to see the babies from the nursery window.

Baby Kim Milsom

I stayed in bed for six days and on the day I had my stitches out, was told I could have a bath. Then I was moved to a ward with two beds and the babies stayed with us all the time, only going into the nursery at night. All the boys were wrapped in blue blankets and the girls in pink.

I remember all us mums lying on the floor and doing exercises to get our stomachs back in shape. It was so nice and clean, the food was good and the nurses were always on hand to help.

A vicar came round once a fortnight. He took a service to give thanks for the safe arrival of the babies. One mum said she was so glad the vicar had done the service because she could then go to her mother-in-law's house, who would be pleased she had been churched!

Beryl Milsom

The 1960s

■ ■ ■ I was given a lift into Stroud Maternity on June 25, 1965, by my gynaecologist, Mr Harry Hamilton, who was a legend around here – a real character.

My husband, Jim, was vicar at Painswick where Harry lived too. The date I was going into hospital had already been decided – I think because he was going away on holiday or something like that – so he said: "I'll be round for you at nine o'clock in the morning."

Well, when I saw him turn up in a low-slung two-seater sports-style car, I couldn't believe it. I thought: "How am I ever going to get into this?" I managed, though I don't know how, and, as he raced around the country bends to Stroud, Harry said: "We'll see if we can have this baby out before we get there!"

*Michael and
Sarah Harris*

He was a naughty old thing, he really was. It's not the most dignified process, lying there with legs strapped up in the air about to be induced. And there he was at the business end when he turned round to me with a wicked grin and said: "I've never seen you looking more attractive." I could have murdered him. But there was nothing I could do and he knew that. He really was a one-off, but he was a great gynaecologist – a very clever man.

When I was due to have my second child in October 1967 we had moved to Gloucester. But I said: "I'm not having this baby unless I can go to Stroud Maternity!" They had been so good when Sarah was born. It was more homely and personal – small is beautiful and all that. Luckily, Dr Jim Hoyland agreed to take me and I also had Michael in Stroud.

I remember Matron Light very well. She once babysat for Sarah and Michael and I could go out and relax completely, knowing the matron of SMH was looking after them!

Pat Harris

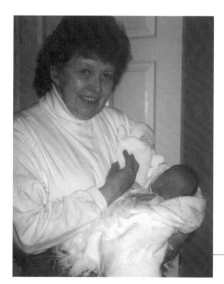

Pat Cook with granddaughter Molly

■ ■ ■ I had an orange for my breakfast, an orange for lunch and, hip, hip hooray, an apple for tea! It was February, 1967. I was only about five months into my second pregnancy and Harry Hamilton, the gynaecologist, thought I was gaining too much weight. I also had high blood pressure, so I was taken into SMH for a few days, to get me going on this apple and orange diet. Needless to say, I came out in spots, my skin was awful, and I didn't like apples and oranges for a long time after.

In the end I think they felt sorry for me. One of the girls who brought the food round gave me a boiled egg one day. She was being kind but unfortunately it wasn't cooked and I couldn't eat it. Once I got out of hospital I was supposed to carry on the diet. But as soon as I got home I used to cheat and buy things like apple turnovers.

Later, when I went into the unit for one of the check-ups, I knew I weighed 12 stone but when I stood on the scales it only registered 11 stone. They said I'd done really well and, although I knew I hadn't lost a stone, I didn't say anything. I just thought let me out of here – I need a cake to celebrate!

I remember Miss Light, the matron. She was nice, very tall and skinny. She told me off once for eating too many strawberries because it can come through in the milk and make the baby colicky.

When visiting my grandchildren, who were born in the late 1990s, I recognised some of the staff who were still working at SMH, including one of the nursery nurses, Else Gager.

Pat Cook

■■■ I was on the books of district nurse Hatherall and didn't go to the hospital or the GP for checks, but to her house. She had a little room in her home where she took blood pressure readings and checked you over. In

Louise Gardiner

those days you'd have your first one in hospital, in case of complications, and could have any others at home.

Ron took me into hospital, in my parents' car – we were living with them at the time. Husbands were not encouraged to stay. I remember being started off by the doctor because I was 10 days overdue and it was a long labour. Because I was a nurse, the matron stayed on to deliver me. She was supposed to be off at 8pm but stayed until I had Louise, just after midnight.

I also had a side ward because of being a nurse. You weren't allowed out of bed for at least five days. I remember being told off once: I'd gone into the bath where they removed alternate stitches from the episiotomy I'd had, and I went to the sitting room afterwards to do my knitting. Well, I was soon marched back to my bed like a naughty little girl.

Diane Gardiner

■ ■ ■ I started off in Stroud with my eldest, Andrew, in February 1967, but was in labour for ages so they shipped me off by ambulance in the middle of the night to Gloucester. I went back to Stroud for aftercare and stayed a long time because it was such a difficult birth. He was a forceps delivery and I had to have blood transfusions. In those days, at 8lb 13oz, Andrew was considered a big baby. I had to sit on a rubber ring for quite a while afterwards. I remember having a bit of a run-in with Matron Light because she was so insistent on breastfeeding. After such a difficult delivery, I just couldn't cope with it. But once the air was cleared between us we got on very well and I loved being in SMH. I couldn't fault it. The nursing care was marvellous.

Andrew, Lee and baby Tracey Marshall

I transferred back to SMH for aftercare with my next two, Lee in 1968 and Tracey in 1970. It made it so much easier for visiting and it was much friendlier there. But the rest were born in Gloucester and I went home straight afterwards. It gets more difficult to stay in hospital when you have little ones at home.

I was back in SMH in December 1995 after the birth of my first grand-daughter, Sophie Haines. I was amazed at all the changes: the decor was bright, the layout totally different and security was very tight. You were allowed only two visitors in the 1960s but they were free to walk in and out.

Pat Marshall

The 1970s

■ ■ ■ All three of my daughters had their children in SMH. We regarded it as our family hospital and felt we belonged. I made some patchwork quilt bed covers which they used for the labour ward beds. My eldest daughter, Elizabeth, had her two sons, Andrew and Jon in 1969 and 1975 and my youngest girl, Janet, had Craig and Daniel there in 1976 and 1979.

When my middle daughter, Sheila, was in labour in April 1970 her husband, Mervyn, said he would give her a bar of chocolate if it was a boy and a pound of sprouts for a girl.

She had Andrea, but haemorrhaged afterwards and had to go over to Gloucester for a transfusion. Later, when she had returned to Stroud, Sheila was sat up in bed when Mervyn handed her a brown paper bag – full of sprouts! Everyone got to know about it because the bag split and they went everywhere. He later produced a large box of chocolates which she shared with the other mums.

Rose Hollis

■ ■ ■ I woke up with very strong and frequent contractions on August 6, 1972, three days before my second daughter, Kim, was born. I rang the hospital and they told me to go in straight away, but by the time I'd settled Tracy with my mum, Kim had decided to go back to sleep. Although the contractions had stopped, when they examined me they found I'd started to dilate, so they kept me in. Tracy had been a small baby and Kim was also early, so they wanted me to hang on as long as possible.

Three days later my husband rang the hospital at 8am to check if anything was happening and because there was no news, he went to work in

Gloucester. Straight after, the contractions started, my waters broke and Kim was born at 9.30. I rang Bruce but he arrived two minutes too late.

When Tracy had been born in Gloucester in 1969 there were complications. I had about eight people with me at the birth but none of them was my husband. I don't think he was too disappointed he didn't make it but I was.

You didn't have your baby next to you. They were brought in for feeding and taken back to the nursery. Rest was considered a high priority for mums. The beds faced out so you could talk across to the other mums. All the beds were being used when I was there and I got to know quite a few people. It was lovely weather and we were able to sit outside. When my doctor came to see me he said: "What do you think this is, a holiday camp?"

During my pregnancy care, I came under the consultant Harry Hamilton. I received fertility treatment with Tracy – in fact, she was the first fertility drug baby in Stroud. Harry Hamilton didn't like his ladies to be overweight and as I was ten-and-a-half stone to start with, I had to be careful. He warned me if I wasn't, he would admit me to hospital on an apple and orange diet. His words kept me trim and because I was so thrilled to be pregnant I would have done anything.

Jan Baker

Jan Baker with daughters
Tracy and Kim

■ ■ ■ The staff were very strict when it came to visiting, because they made us rest in the afternoon. They were friendly and helpful and, if you didn't understand anything, they would show you what to do.

By the time my third child, Terry, was born at SMH on December 28, 1972, I knew what I was doing and was in for just a few days.

A nursery nurse used to show you how to bath the baby and, on the third bath, you would do it with them watching. My ex-husband wasn't at the birth because I needed him to look after our other two.

SMH is more like a family unit than a hospital and it would be lovely to see my grandchildren born there.

Janet Bowkett

■ ■ ■ I'd catch the bus from the quietness of Hampton Fields to Stroud's bustling bus station, then rush up the hill to SMH. I took an instant dislike to the sister at the last appointment before my confinement when she told me it might be two weeks before I had my baby. It was not what I'd wanted to hear. I was so fed up, particularly with people telling me how large I was.

Fortunately, two days later, my labour started. But it took a while for Becky to arrive on January 28, 1972. My contractions had gone off the boil and Dr Somervell said he would start me off and break my waters. He nicked the bag and, whoosh, there was water all over the floor. I was on the narrowest and hardest of labour beds and it was so high up I was frightened I'd fall off.

My husband, who never did listen, decided when I should have the gas and air and clamped the mask on my face whenever he thought it was needed. I eventually wrenched the mask off him and it broke in two.

I saw Becky only briefly immediately after she was born. Then Dr Booth performed what he called "some embroidery" on my nether regions. I had a cup of tea and went to sleep, obviously still under the influence of the gas and air. I woke to a ward of clattering metal and cups – but where were the babies?

And then they came. En masse. The babies were lined up on a scrubbed wooden trolley which glided through the ward like a sleigh. Pink heads peeped out from the top of snowy blankets and I was handed this rigid parcel. And then love overwhelmed me for this little creature.

Breastfeeding took tenacity and time. Stroud had the answer to sore nipples – they were painted with Friars Balsam. It was sticky and brown and tasted disgustingly bitter. I know, I tried it and was surprised any babies suckled at all. I was glad I stayed in for 10 days. I was grateful of the sleep for there were no night-time feeds. The babies stayed in the nursery and were given water. They had to know their place and it was in the nursery, out of earshot.

Our ward was kept scrupulously tidy and clean and we'd scatter like tiny children to our bedsides if matron was about to come in. For the first couple of days I think we had to stay in bed and perform all toiletry requirements perched on a bedpan behind a swathe of floral curtains. This required a degree of balance worthy of a tightrope walker.

Visiting time was looked forward to with anticipation. We were not allowed to walk around when the visitors were there, and always had to have our housecoats on when sitting out of bed. One day I didn't have a visitor, so I sneaked out to the nursery, having ascertained that matron was not around. I wanted to take another peep at Becky to make sure she was all right. A new father was already in the nursery inspecting his newborn baby.

"Oh, hello," I said. "Lovely baby!" "Yes," he smiled proudly and, observing my pink quilted shape, asked: "And when are you expecting yours?"

Little did I know that I would return to SMH the following two years for the births of Andre (June 2, 1973) and Clara (November 27, 1974). I got the hang of it in the end.

Jacquie Govier

Becky, Andre and Clara Govier

■ ■ ■   When I had Lucy in November 1974 I stayed in 14 days because she had jaundice. They were all very nice. I met Jacquie Govier, in with her third baby, Clara, and we became friends. The food was all right but I think the last meal was around 5pm. One night, a few days after our babies were born, we were both feeling a bit peckish. Well, my uncle was visiting so he popped into Stroud and got us some takeaway chicken and chips. It was lovely.

My daughter, Clare, made a speedy arrival at Stroud. I went into the hospital at 6.10 and she was born 15 minutes later. My husband, Barry, had to scoot along the corridor a bit quick and only just made it in time for her birth.

I went to visit Clare when she had Jacob in SMH on February 17, 1999, and there had obviously been huge changes since I was in. Everyone had their own little bays with curtains whereas there had been very little privacy before.

Sue Martin

■ ■ ■   I had varied experiences of childbirth in the 1970s, including a very sad experience at SMH.

My first little boy was born in Gloucester. At that time partners were banned from being present at a forceps delivery, which was how Paul arrived in 1973. I'd had high blood pressure and stayed at Stroud for four days before he was born.

Two years later, I had a girl at SMH. It was particularly special because she was the first baby born on New Year's Day, 1975, and the local newspapers came to take photographs. My husband was there for the birth which, in comparison to my first experience, went really well. But when Rosamund was just a couple of days old they realised there was something wrong. Dr Kelly said they thought there was a problem and we were transferred to Gloucester. There it became more serious and Rosamund was transferred to Bristol, while I had to stay in Gloucester.

She died after an operation. She had an aneurysm, near the brain, but had initially seemed perfectly normal. If she hadn't been a New Year's Day baby I wouldn't have had any photographs. We were too late to stop The Citizen using the photo but the Stroud News and Journal didn't print it and kindly sent us a copy. I still get upset, thinking of her. It's something that stays with you.

A year and a month later I had another boy, in Gloucester because of what had happened to Rosamund. Nicholas was born on February 2, 1976. I went back to SMH afterwards and stayed for eight days. I found the

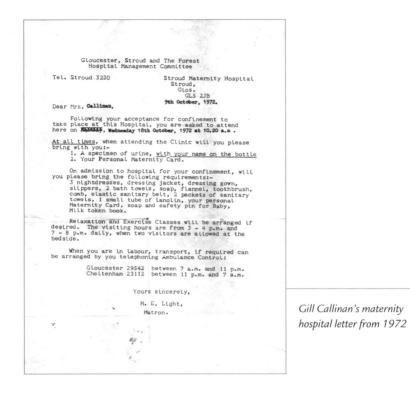

Gill Callinan's maternity
hospital letter from 1972

atmosphere more relaxed at Stroud. Then I had Laura at SMH in 1979 and that was fine, so I ended up having a good birth experience at Stroud.

It is nice that I now work part-time at SMH as ward clerk in the midwives' office, answering the phone and dealing with paperwork.

Gill Callinan

■ ■ ■ When our daughter, Elizabeth, was married on June 21, 2003, her father referred to her birth at SMH in his wedding speech, saying she had shown all the characteristics of being an easy-going 'Stroudie' ever since her birth at a very laidback unit on July 2, 1978.

When we got to the hospital, I was taken to a small side ward and Peter was told to ring the bell if we needed the midwife. Within minutes I could feel the head being born and Peter rang the bell but no one came. He rang again without response so he ran to the night desk where he found out the bell wasn't working!

I was transferred to a wheelchair and we hurtled down to the delivery room like something out of *ER*, where Elizabeth was born with a rush. In the end, everything was well and the staff could not have been kinder.

Denise Gibson

Elizabeth Gibson

The 1980s

■ ■ ■ I started having my eldest son, Jonathan, in Stroud, but the contractions stopped so I went to bed. Steve, my husband, was put in the room next to me so he could have a sleep and in the morning, when the nurses came

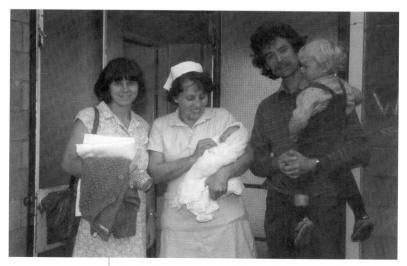

Carrie, Steve and Jonathan Dorey with nursing auxiliary, Teresa Lautieri, holding baby Mark

round, they knocked on his door and brought him an enema for a joke. He was very amused by the whole thing.

The labour was prolonged and I had to go to Gloucester to be induced, but came back to SMH for aftercare. I thought it was wonderful, so friendly, kind and homely. June Strange was a friend and working as a nursery nurse when I had Mark, so it was lovely to have her at hand. The food was good and we used to have post-natal physio to help get our stomachs and pelvic muscles back in trim. All the mums did it together. We'd all lie on our beds and follow the instructions with a lot of hilarity. They were also quite insistent we had to go to bed after lunch and rest.

I used to be a sister at Stroud General so it was nice to see all the doctors around and nursing friends could come and visit easily. I wished I could have had all my children in SMH, but moved to Gloucester in 1985 so naturally had my last two there.

Carrie Dorey

Baby Pauline Hensley

■ ■ ■ It was not quite midnight when the call came. The small flat over a shop in Southall suddenly became busy as I dressed and stuffed a few items into my suitcase. Midnight passed into January 17, 1980. It was a cold night and freezing fog hung in patches along the M4 as I sped west towards SMH, to my wife and our third expected child.

The Cirencester to Stroud road was, as always, a nightmare and it was now well past 1am. Our first daughter had taken eight hours to arrive and our second about four, so I hoped I would be in time to welcome our third into the world as I had the first two.

I negotiated the steep hill up to SMH, and eventually found my way to the door in the pitch black, but our third daughter had beaten me to it. I was ushered to the bedside to see the proud mum with our new bundle of mischief. Tea and biscuits were gratefully received, provided by the wonderful staff, who were constant in their care and devotion to duty. Now our daughters are much older, I wonder whether I will be called upon to dash to a future bedside as a grandfather. I just hope they get the same care and attention we experienced at SMH in the '70s and '80s.

Richard Hensley

The 1990s

■ ■ ■ My GP asked if I was going to Gloucester or Cheltenham to have my first baby. When I said I was going to Stroud I was made to feel it was an inappropriate decision for a first birth as "you never know what is going to happen". There was no discussion of the options available and no mention of either home birth or SMH. I later discovered many women are not given all the options.

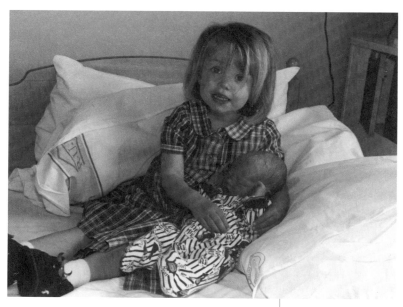

Abi and baby Isaac

Abi was born in SMH after a long second stage. The midwives were brilliant in making suggestions and helping me change position.

When she was about 16 months old the future of the unit was under review and I remember feeling very strongly it should stay open. There's no other service like it in the area and it's extremely important it remains a viable option.

As a member of Stroud Valleys National Childbirth Trust I became involved in the 1998 campaign to save SMH. Following its success, the unit was given targets to meet on both deliveries and post-natal care. So when I became pregnant soon afterwards I decided to have my second baby in Stroud, rather than at home. Isaac was born in the birthing pool at SMH – a very gentle introduction into the world.

Marianne Orr

■ ■ ■ I started off in Stroud with Hannah but had to transfer to Gloucester after 15 hours because I didn't dilate. The midwife followed behind in a car and the ambulance journey has stayed in my mind because the young and inexperienced paramedic said: "Please don't have it in here. I won't know what to do!"

The labour lasted 28 hours in the end, before Hannah arrived on April 1, 1995.

I went back after two or three days to Stroud and can remember sitting round the table with a group of mums, having a laugh and a joke with Nursery Nurse June Strange. She was telling a story about how a hamster had died in a jar. Rigor mortis had set in and June was demonstrating how she had tried to shake it out. I was crying with laughter and begging her to stop because my bum was in agony, with stitches in dire danger of popping.

But she just kept going and going with this tale and I had to leave the breakfast table in the end because it was too painful. I think it turned out that the hamster in the story hadn't been dead after all!

I'd had all sorts of problems having Hannah, including a blood transfusion, so was feeling tremendously vulnerable after such a traumatic time. I cried when I first got to SMH and June was there because we had been friends for a long time and it was such a relief to see her. I felt so safe and secure seeing someone I knew.

Helen Leatherland

■ ■ ■ William, our first son, was due on December 27, 1995. At the time my husband and I were living in Fulham, London. I had gone through all my antenatal care there and found the support adequate, but not very personal. I grew up in the Stroud area, knew SMH's reputation and really hoped I would go into labour over the Christmas period while I was visiting my parents, so I could give birth in Stroud.

I was set to travel back to London on the day William was due, but all the time quietly hoped to go into labour before I left. Well, my wish came

Sarah Murphy and son William

true. Around midnight on the 26th my contractions started and, thinking that babies come along quickly, I went straight down to SMH. My husband and I arrived and I said: "I'm having a baby. You don't know who I am, but I'm having it here."

The initial response was that I had plenty of time to get back to London, so should jump in a car. But there was no way I was moving. I spent the rest of the night and the day of the 27th in the labour ward and in the bath down the corridor. My labour progressed slowly but without problems. I coped well with the pain using gas and air and am convinced that being so relaxed and comfortable in my surroundings contributed to my easy labour. Towards evening it became clear William was stuck and I was getting more and more exhausted. The decision was made that I needed an episiotomy and forceps delivery. My midwife at that stage was Michelle Poole and I was completely happy to go along with whatever she said.

The beds in the hospital are incredible. They are like something out of a James Bond film with the different positions they can be put into. It was certainly amazing how they got my legs at right angles to my body! I do yoga but there's no way I could have got into that sort of position without the aid of the two poles that magically appeared out of the end of the bed.

There was great excitement when the TV doctor Mark Porter arrived to do the delivery. Well, he saw me at my best! Apparently I bled all over his suede shoes, although I have no recollection of that. Anyway, William was delivered safely on December 27 and my dream was realised. Dr Porter did such a neat job of sewing me up afterwards. Since then I've had two more boys, both born at SMH. The staff are wonderful and the births are magical experiences that I recollect daily.

Sarah Murphy

■ ■ ■ I gave birth to Harriet in Gloucester on May 17, 1996, but went back to Stroud the next day where the care was so good that I didn't want to go home. I felt safe there.

Becoming a new mum was such an unknown and I was quite happy to stay in SMH until my milk came in. It was such a lovely atmosphere – like a holiday camp for mothers with their new babies.

One night, a baby was crying but his mother was snoring and in such a deep sleep that she couldn't hear him. Well, we all could and one of the night staff had to wake her up. We were all envious she could sleep so deeply.

Lynn Stride

▓ ▓ ▓ I have this lasting impression of me sitting on a rocking chair, concentrating on the ever-increasing contractions, while Graham, my husband, and the midwife, Sue Hill, dashed in and out with buckets of water. It was June 14, 1996, and part of my plan for labour at SMH was to use the birthing pool – only, at that time, it was more like a swimming pool.

When I'd arrived it was apparent I was quite a way on already and if I was going to use the pool at all it would need to be filled quickly. It was and I found it wonderful for helping with Emma's arrival.

By the time my second child, Tom, was born on January 3, 1999, the new birthing pool was installed, but unfortunately I didn't have enough time to use it. When I arrived, the midwife showed me to the delivery room and suggested I took half an hour to settle in. I still looked very much in control but could tell things were progressing fast so I asked her to check me. Tom was born just 20 minutes later.

One of my memories was carrying my newborn child around to the ward where they had saved me Sunday lunch. One of the nursery nurses cuddled my son while I sat and ate and it seemed quite surreal to be enjoying my lunch less than two hours after arrival at the unit.

Fiona Gill

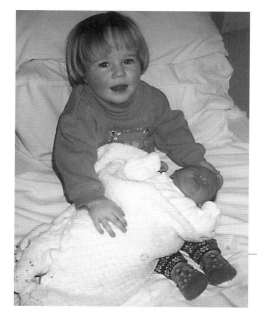

Emma and Tom Gill

■ ■ ■ Two things really struck me when I was in Stroud for aftercare with my first baby, Sam, in June 1996.

One was that there were no baby girls at all. There were five other mums and we all had boys. I remember asking one of the staff if that was usual. In a broad Gloucestershire accent she answered there must be a war brewing – which is not what you want to hear when you've just had a new baby.

The second memory was when Sam was a couple of days old. It was the hottest day of the year, absolutely roasting, and I had him in a vest, baby grow and cardigan, because I didn't know what you should do with a baby – I thought you had to keep them warm.

He'd gone red and blotchy so I asked one of the nursery staff if he was okay. I'll never forget her reply: "I know they look good enough to eat, but you don't have to cook them first!"

Clare Hankey

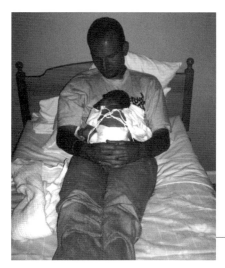

Clare's husband Pete with son Sam

■ ■ ■ I was due to go to Gloucester with my second baby. Luckily, I put a towel on the car seat because as we set off, just after midnight on September 24, 1996, my waters broke at the Ebley roundabout. I told my husband, Neil, I didn't think I'd make it to Gloucester so we turned around and headed to SMH.

The midwife calmly took us straight to a delivery room. As my soggy leggings came down she said: "Oh, you are well on the way, I can see the head – better get you up on the bed."

I had a 7lb 2oz baby boy 13 minutes after arriving at SMH. Some uncomfortable stitching was followed by a welcome cup of tea and a sandwich. The patient reassurances of the amazingly calm midwife were exactly what I needed after the shock of such a fast birth.

Sue Thompson

■ ■ ■ It was lovely. I was so relaxed having Henry there in August 1999. Everybody who has the chance to, should go. There's a lot of pressure from some GPs, who say it's not safe, and try to persuade mums to go to bigger units. Mine tried to. But I don't think women should listen to doctors who obviously haven't done their homework. The midwives at Stroud all have to be very experienced to work there.

Henry was born during the evening of a huge thunderstorm. It had been a really hot day and the windows were open, so the floor got wet and Andy, my husband, slipped over in the corridor. I also remember that after Henry was born Andy and the midwife were having a discussion over what time to put down for the birth and couldn't agree, so I interrupted and decided it had been 8.28!

Cath Cox

■ ■ ■ Your first baby is so special, and every moment of labour, birth and those early days should be cherished. Precious time.

My son Matthew was born in Gloucester, after a long but straightforward labour. I still remember the astonishment of how, after that final searing push, I looked down on the bed and saw a beautiful, dark haired, perfect baby boy.

At that time, no one knew how ill he really was. His little heart, which seemed to beat so strongly, was badly mal-formed.

We went back to SMH, the same day, for some rest and recuperation. It was home from home. It was lovely, as always, to see old friends and make new ones: post-natal mums all sitting together, making tea and toast, comparing our sore bits, sleeping habits and our beautiful babies. We were so proud and nervous.

An ever-cheerful Michelle Poole showed me how to bath and swaddle him. I remember pushing him down the corridor to the nursery in his little plastic cot. We dozed, fed, bathed, chatted and I showed him to visitors. The small cubicle in the ward filled up with cards and flowers, huge bouquets of carnations and lilies from his daddy and from work. Their scent grew stronger in the August heat.

Then home, carefully in the car seat, to his newly decorated room. New furniture, new wallpaper, the smell of lilies mingling with baby powder. We slept there, Matthew and I, looking at the lovely flowers when we woke, and breathing in their heady scent. Ten days later he was in intensive care, awaiting surgery. Three weeks later he died.

After I packed away the baby clothes I didn't go into that bedroom for months. I can't bear the smell of lilies. When Ellen was born a year later, and Jim three years later, I had different flowers.

Thank you Stroud Maternity for that short, happy time.

My other children were strong and healthy and born without intervention, one in Gloucester and one in Stroud.

Katharine McNealey

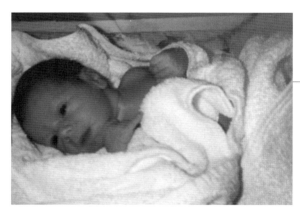

*Baby Matthew
McNealey*

New Millennium

■ ■ ■ Eddie's birth on April 14, 2000, was lovely from start to finish. I can honestly say it was perfect and everything I wanted it to be. My labour was seven-and-a-half hours long and I was able to use the water pool during it. I had two midwives, who were very different in their approaches, and I needed both. There was a struggle to get Eddie out in the end because his head turned at the last minute, and the midwife coached me through the final pushes. I later found out his head was on the 98th centile in size for newborns.

It was very relaxing and quiet in Stroud. I felt I could ask for anything. They were reassuring and put me at ease afterwards when I delivered the placenta. My whole stay was positive and I had lots of help with breast-feeding. I was shown how to feed Eddie underarm which is how I did it until he got too long.

In our antenatal classes, the men were told they would have to pack a bag too. Steve, Eddie's dad, packed his paints and sketchbook because he thought he would be in the hospital for hours, but never got them out. He didn't even eat his sandwiches.

Karen Saunders

Karen Saunders and baby Eddie

■ ■ ■ My eldest son, Blayne, was born nine weeks early on July 2, 1992. It was frightening as he was my first baby and only weighed 3lb 14oz and was in special care for a month. I was not well again when Tyler was born seven-and-a-half weeks premature, at 5lb 6oz. On both occasions the staff at Gloucester's special care baby unit were very supportive and kind.

But when my third son, Elliott, was born on November 10, 2000, three days overdue, it was a huge relief finally to get to SMH. I gave up work at 18 weeks and I'm sure that really helped the pregnancy.

Tyler, Blayne and baby Elliott Wherrett

My midwife, Jo Morris, was fantastic. Because of what happened with Blayne and Tyler, I obviously didn't have my own midwife delivering in Gloucester and found that so scary. Jo knew how frightened I was and went on call for me with Elliott. They rang her when I got into SMH and she came down straight away and delivered him. I just felt so secure with her. It was a familiar face, which is exactly what I needed. I'm just so glad I made it there and it was so lovely I stayed for five days. I didn't want to come out! They readily took the babies if you needed a rest or a bath and I felt very much at home. We are so lucky to have the unit. I'd nearly go so far as to say I thoroughly enjoyed it!

My mum went back to SMH for aftercare with my younger brother, Liam. She must have been in there a while because she used to sit out on the balcony and came out with a suntan!

Mel Wherrett

▦ ▦ ▦ Joshua was a surprise breech, and it was not until he was coming out – bottom first – that the midwives realised. In fact, one of the midwives was so shaken up that she couldn't deliver another baby for two weeks.

In the end, there were four midwives and an ambulance man in the room with me. Once Joshua was born we were rushed to Gloucester because he was very blue, and he had to go into intensive care for 24 hours.

I had an overwhelming feeling that he would be okay and, when I went back to SMH, the aftercare was wonderful.

Angela Carroll

▦ ▦ ▦ I had a show at 10pm and rang the midwife and she suggested I should go in. I went with my husband, Steve, at about 2am on October 16, 2001. I was only a quarter-of-a-centimetre dilated so she said to go back home, relax, have a bath and return at breakfast time. By six o'clock my labour pains were quite intense and I found the most comfortable place to be was on the loo.

Katrina Perrins and son Nathaniel

It must have been just gone seven when I felt something pop. I got Steve to have a look and he said part of the sack had come outside – it was like a white balloon full of water. The waters hadn't burst. He rang the hospital and I went straight in. The pains were very intense by that stage. I had discussed having a water birth, so when I arrived the midwife on duty, Sue Williams, went off to run the birthing pool. But when she examined me she went off to get another midwife and said there was no time for a water birth and I had better start pushing. Less than 15 minutes and five pushes later Nathaniel arrived and my waters were still intact.

The midwife told me I'd had a dry birth and, according to midwife tales, the baby would never drown. She also said it was just as well I had gone in, otherwise he would have been born down the toilet. The irony is that I had wanted a water birth, but ended up having a dry birth with no water in sight! But it made no difference to Nathaniel. He absolutely loves the water now.

Katrina Perrins

▨ ▨ ▨ I had planned to give birth in Gloucester but, because there was a blizzard, couldn't get there and had to settle for Stroud instead. It was a blessing in disguise.

There had been this incredible snowstorm in the middle of the night. It was quite dramatic, and we couldn't see any road markings. I had rung Gloucester to say I was on my way, but we couldn't get there, so went to Stroud, even though they didn't know I was coming.

They offered to call an ambulance and put chains on the wheels so that it gripped the roads, but my husband Andy wouldn't have been able to travel with me, so we decided to stay at SMH. I was so impressed with the care. As long as there are no complications during labour, I think all women should go there because it is such a relaxing place. The care is second to none and, if there are complications, they can transfer to Gloucester.

I'd opted for Gloucester because I had wanted an epidural. Looking back, I'm so glad I couldn't get there. I found the atmosphere, care and attention in Stroud more than made up for it.

Suzanne Brook, whose daughter Miah-Mae was born in December 2000

▨ ▨ ▨ Harrison was 11 days late when he was born in SMH, and I'd had to go backwards and forwards to the hospital for check-ups.

I went in at 1am and they examined me, but nothing much was happening. I was due to be induced two days later, but as we drove home, the contractions started strongly and we were back in Stroud soon afterwards. It was nice knowing the hospital was nearby. I had a natural birth, with no need for painkillers. Harrison was 10lb and I didn't need any stitches.

People are quite amazed by that, but I'm sure it was down to the skill of the midwife. Once he was born I had my tea and toast and a lovely bath without, at last, feeling like an elephant.

It was so quiet in SMH. While I was having Harrison, an extension was being built on our house. It was like a building site, so it was such a relief not to have drills going or banging and crashing. That's why I opted to have a side room. I really needed peace and quiet because I knew it would be chaos once I got home. It was like being in a cocoon. People used to joke: "You're not going to go home, are you?"

I'd had Lois in Gloucester, in 2000, but went back to Stroud. It reminded me of being on a school trip or at girls' camp, having all our meals together. We really felt looked after and they gave us nice puddings.

We are so privileged to have SMH. I have friends who had their babies elsewhere and it is just incomparable. It would be horrible to lose it.

Cathy Brown, former health visitor

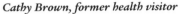

Ben and Cathy Brown with Lois and Harrison

■ ■ ■ When I had my first daughter, Caitlin, I transferred from Gloucester to Stroud. Without SMH I wouldn't have met so many of the friends I still see. It's so nice for the children to grow up with friends they've known from birth.

SMH is such a cosy, family environment. I felt like I was being looked after by my mum – lots of home cooking and being told to rest in the afternoon. The dads are made to feel very much part of the whole experience too.

When Amy was born in the labour lasted almost 24 hours. They had to go over to the general hospital to get more canisters of gas and air because I got through so many! I wanted to labour in water. Having back problems, I knew it would support me. I was happy in the pool and stayed in for quite a long time. I found it very relaxing – it gave me more mobility and I could get in different positions.

I was so glad I had Amy in Stroud because I wanted to add to the hospital's figures to help ensure it stayed open.

Jackie Smalley

■ ■ ■ When Sean was born at SMH, on November 29, 2002, there was what they call a true knot in the umbilical cord, which is very rare. Had it been detected by the scan, I probably wouldn't have been allowed to have him in Stroud. The midwife was amazed and said she had only ever seen one other example of it.

I'd had my first son, Ciaran, in St George's Hospital in London, which was more of a production line. I couldn't believe the stories I heard about Stroud. It sounded too good to be true and one friend told me you could always tell a great hospital if they ask you whether you want brown or white toast for breakfast. So when I got asked that question, I couldn't stop laughing. It really felt like I was in the Hotel Stroud Maternity.

Jo McLoughlin

Jo's husband Stephen Bryden with son Sean and the true knot

■ ■ ■ I'd had wonderful aftercare at SMH after the birth of my second baby, Lucy, and my first night back at Stroud with Rosie, born on March 14, 2003, was Comic Relief night. During visiting, my husband, Scott, and I had been talking about how strapped for cash we were going to be with three children. Then he went home and celebrated Rosie's safe arrival with a couple of glasses of wine, in front of the television. When he came in the next morning he told me he'd made a donation on behalf of Jack, Lucy and Rosie. Our conversation went something like this:

Jack and baby Rosie Curtis

Me: "Oh well done, that's good."
Him: "There was one clip about a brother and sister living on the
         streets in Africa and the little girl was the same age as Lucy."
Me: *(on verge of tears)*: "That's terrible. Poor little thing . . ."
Him: "It made me think about how lucky we are. . . "
Me: "How much did you donate?"
Him: "One hundred pounds. . . "
Me: Speechless for once!

Debbie Curtis

▣ ▣ ▣ Isabel was the only baby born on the 50th anniversary of SMH, March 30, 2003. It was great timing as she arrived on Mothering Sunday – a wonderful present. My husband, Andrew, and I were given a silver spoon to mark the occasion by the League of Friends. It was presented the following day by Diane Clewes, a supporter of the league who was born at SMH in 1953. Isabel arrived at 2.30am, just four hours after we got to SMH, pretty fast for a first baby.

Alex Billington

Baby Isabel Billington

10 · THROUGH THE GENERATIONS

P HYLLIS HOGG'S daughter Yvonne Tudor was SMH's first Easter baby on April 5, 1953. Her granddaughter, Tracey, was born at SMH on Easter Saturday, 1973, granddaughter Jemma on October 18, 1983 and great grandson Callum in February 1993.

■ ■ ■ I was the first to have an Easter Sunday baby in SMH. There were four of us in a six-bed ward and we were treated like royalty. We were given cream cakes with our morning drink but were told we wouldn't get them when more patients came in.

The birth was very quick. I got to Stroud at six in the morning and had Yvonne at seven. My husband wasn't allowed in at the birth but he came to see me during the evening visiting, 6-8pm.

My son, Geoffrey, was two at the time but he wasn't allowed in, so I didn't see him for the two weeks I stayed in. I left him with my sister-in-law.

I had my third child, Adrian, in an old cottage in Horsley. I didn't want to leave the other two, which is why I opted for a home birth instead.

The meals were very good in SMH – it was lovely. The matron at the time was lovely, too. She was the matron in Tetbury when I'd had my first baby and she remembered me.

Phyllis Hogg

■ ■ ■ It's a brilliant homely hospital – more like a hotel. My husband wasn't at the birth out of choice, not because he couldn't be. He was too squeamish. I had my two boys in Gloucester afterwards, a choice taken out of my hands, but it wasn't the same as Stroud.

It's rather special that four of our family members were born in SMH on the anniversary decades. I'm 50 this year, my daughter's 30, my niece is 20 and my great nephew is 10, so we represent babies born over the five decades. Times have moved on but the care over the years has been second to none.

Yvonne Tudor

Gaynor Dowdeswell's daughter, Lynne Woodman, was born at SMH on June 1, 1955. Lynne gave birth to her daughter Lisa Everitt at SMH on November 11, 1975 and Lisa's daughter Katie was born at SMH on October 15, 2001.

■ ■ ■ I was in a large ward. We were all in one big room and couldn't go home for two weeks after our babies were born. For the first week we weren't even allowed to make our beds.

The babies were kept in the nursery and we only saw them at feeding and visiting times. We didn't think anything of it then – those were the rules and we accepted them. It meant we had plenty of rest and made a full recovery so we could go home and cope.

Four generations: (from left) Lynne Woodman, Lisa Everitt and Gaynor Dowdeswell and baby Katie (front)

The staff at Stroud were lovely. I can remember Sister Costervan and Nurse Wright. I wanted a June baby. I was told she would be born in May, but had a 36-hour labour and Lynne was born at 2am on June 1.

My husband was away working at the time. He saw Lynne for the first time when she was five days old.

The matron was strict but very nice. She was a lady you could admire. She would not take any nonsense. As long as you did what she said, she was very sweet. I think it was better then than it is now. It certainly provided good foundations for motherhood.

Gaynor Dowdeswell

■ ■ ■ Lisa was late so I had to go into Stroud to have my waters broken, to get started. My GP came in to do it, but I didn't go into labour all that day. I was in a room on my own and went into the big ward that afternoon to watch *Crossroads*. A lady in the ward suggested I should jump up and down. So while I was watching *Crossroads*, and when the midwives couldn't see me, I did. Sure enough, I went into labour after that and had her at 10 o'clock in the evening.

The care was good and it was very different to when I had my first child, Mark, in Gloucester. I started off in Stroud on the Monday evening and went to Gloucester on the Wednesday. I was only 17 at the time and was looked down upon because I was so young. I remember Miss Light, who was matron, saying: "It serves you right that you're in labour so long. You shouldn't be doing this sort of thing – you should be playing with your dolls at 17."

I'll never forget what she said. She certainly made sure you knew what she thought. When I had Lisa I was married and it was so different.

Lynne Woodman

■ ■ ■ There were quite a few births the day I had Katie. In fact, one of my friends had to go into the monitoring room to have her baby because it was so busy and full. Even though they were rushed off their feet, the staff were really helpful.

I had a frustrating time breastfeeding and they were very patient. We tried everything, but Katie just didn't want to feed. The staff were really caring and there when you needed them.

There was a student nurse around during my birth who was very kind. She held one of my hands and my husband, Steve, held the other. I was asked if I'd like to use the water pool, but by the time it had been filled, I'd progressed very quickly and didn't have time. Hospitals are usually clinical, but I didn't feel I was in one at all. It was very comfortable, a real home from home.

Lisa Everitt

Fred and Audrey Robson's daughter, Liz Hudson, was born at SMH on September 24, 1953. Liz had her three children in SMH – Victoria, Gregory and Judith.

■ ■ ■ Men didn't attend childbirth at all. It was none of our business. I think it's great nowadays, exactly how it should be. People should share everything, just as long as they don't ask me to!

There was no bonding as such with your child until the next day. I wasn't encouraged to change nappies and there was no time off work. I was in production control at Daniel's and had to ring up to find out if my wife, Audrey, had had Liz yet.

The first time I went back to the hospital was when Liz gave birth to the first of her three children, who were all born in SMH. It was a far more relaxed atmosphere. It was quite regimented when Liz was born, but Audrey had been a nursing sister and a maternity nurse, so she accepted those things.

Fred Robson

■ ■ ■ I was in Stroud about 10 days and enjoyed my stay. In those days we were encouraged to have our babies at home. I wanted to have her at home, but was living in Stonehouse with my parents so I went to SMH.

If I had Liz nowadays, I still wouldn't want my husband at the birth. I think it should be for the woman. There's no need for husbands to be there. Just let the woman get on with it.

Audrey Robson

■ ■ ■ When I had my eldest, Victoria, I was more worried about being in a ward with other people than the prospect of labour as it was my first time in hospital and I'd never shared a bedroom. But when I got there it was brilliant. I found I wasn't the only one suffering after having stitches and it was great to talk to others.

I remember they had this super loo which you had to use within 24 hours of giving birth and, after you had done your business, you would press various buttons and it would give you a wash and blow dry. It was most peculiar, but I don't think it lasted long. I certainly didn't use it when I had Gregory in 1983. I only stayed in five days with him, compared to 10 with Victoria. The care was brilliant. I breastfed all my children, even though they weren't keen initially. The staff gave me lots of encouragement, which really helped.

With Judith in 1988, I went in the previous afternoon and although the contractions had stopped, the midwives decided to keep me in. All of sudden at 1am they started again in earnest. The midwives asked me for my husband's phone number. I gave them the wrong number so they phoned this bloke telling him his wife was in labour and he'd better come quickly! His wife was in bed with him at the time. Eventually they looked up my notes and rang the right number. I don't think he's ever moved so fast in his life.

The babies would stay with the mums all day, but go into the nursery at night. If you were breastfeeding, the nurse would come and fetch you to feed the baby in the nursery so as not to disturb everyone else. That way you were guaranteed some sleep.

It would be fantastic if my grandchildren were born there.

Liz Hudson

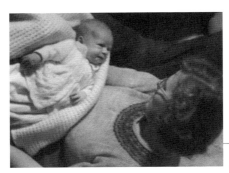

Audrey with baby Liz

Judy Mills' son, Nick, was born at SMH in April 1962. Jill Watkins' daughter Louise, Nick's wife, was born there in 1968. Louise had four of their five children at SMH.

▓ ▓ ▓ I had all my three in SMH. Nick was my first, in April 1962. We lived at Houndscroft behind the Bear of Rodborough and my husband took me in for all three. But in those days they didn't see the babies born – it makes him go funny behind the knees! It certainly made me go funny.

Sister Murrow delivered Nick. Dr Newton had said to me: "When I see you again it will be in Stroud Maternity Hospital." And he was right. He was a good old-fashioned doctor. He knew when the babies were coming.

If the baby was the wrong way round he'd turn it ready. My mother had Dr Newton and he kept turning her baby but it kept turning back. He just kept turning it the other way again – he was wonderful.

Sister Wright delivered my second in June 1965 and I had Matron Light and her assistant for the last baby in July 1968. It was a smashing hospital, friendly and caring. The lovely nurses were understanding and had time for the patients. All the meals were made on the premises. It was wonderful.

Judy Mills

■ ■ ■ When I had Louise, I remember my husband Bryn coming in with his flashy camera and the ladies in the ward thought he was a press photographer. He wasn't there for the birth.

My waters broke at midnight and we didn't have a phone so had to go out to the phone box in the street outside. They told us to go in straight away. Bryn stayed with me for a while but then went to work. He often says now he wished he'd stayed. He was there at the births of our other two children.

It wasn't quite as popular then to have your husbands with you. Louise was due on September 18 but came on August 22. Although she was a month early it didn't seem a problem to have her at Stroud then. The staff were very pleasant and I have very good memories. I still see some of the mums around Stroud whom I met in hospital 35 years ago.

Jill Watkins

■ ■ ■ Sophie was four-and-a-half weeks early so we had to go to Gloucester where all 6lb of her arrived on December 8, 1992. I transferred back to SMH as soon as I could and went home when she was a week old, as you do with your first, because it's a luxury, isn't it? It was just before the refurbishment and I spent some time in the labour side of the hospital before being moved into a room off the corridor. I thought it was so welcoming and friendly. They really tried to get me breastfeeding without being pushy, and they succeeded. I fed them all until they were a year old and Arthur until he was two. I remember being engorged when my milk came in and one of the staff advised me to put cabbage leaves on my breasts.

After Harriet I had Amelia – and I got to the hospital with just four minutes to spare. The midwife was in the room on her own and didn't even have time to undo the delivery pack. We had arrived at 3.30am and Amelia was born at 3.34! The next morning one of the other mums said: "Did you nearly have your baby in the car park? It's not fair – I was in labour 24 hours."

Isobel arrived three weeks early. I just made it into Stroud as they won't take deliveries before 37 weeks. By then I was just staying two nights. A lady came from a Bristol hospital with twins and she had been advised to go to Stroud because of the aftercare. They were so good, helping her breastfeed them both.

I wasn't going to have any more but then thought as we needed a seven-seater car we may as well have one more. When the lady doing the scan told us it was a boy, my husband, Nick, nearly fell off the chair! They pretty much left me to my own devices with Arthur. The staff would come in and chat about the TV rather than the baby. The policy had changed again a bit by then. They didn't seem to mind if I kept the baby in bed with me once I'd fed him. I was also in the same room as when I'd had Sophie, which was lovely.

Louise Mills

11 · BORN BEFORE ARRIVAL

*Diane and Mike
Harris with Molly and
baby Katie*

I WAS TRYING TO get into our car when our second daughter, Katie, was born on the road outside our house in Butterrow Lane on December 17, 1998. It was a cold winter's day and I was devastated as I had been determined she should be born at SMH to boost the threatened unit's figures.

I'm never early myself, so could not believe how quickly she arrived. We had been down to the unit an hour or so before everything really kicked off and my midwife had told us not to worry as the cervix hadn't even begun to dilate.

We were a bit concerned because our elder daughter Molly's birth at SMH in May 1996 had been quick for a first baby. I will never forget the midwife saying with an all-knowing smile: "These babies don't just drop out you know." Well, Katie did.

Just over an hour later the contractions suddenly increased in intensity. My only concern was to get into SMH as I wanted a water birth and knew it took quite a while to fill the pool.

I started walking up the 20 steps from our Victorian semi. Halfway up, my husband Mike informed me an ambulance and midwife were on the way and I should go back indoors. But why would I walk back down the steps only to have two ambulance men carry me back up? I decided to struggle on up and meet them at the top.

Once there, we decided to head for SMH, a four-minute drive away, as our car was parked just across the narrow lane. I got as far as opening the door when another contraction hit me. At no point did I feel I was pushing. If anything, I was doing my pelvic floor exercises. I thought I couldn't have the baby without a midwife. But I could and did.

While all this was going on – out of sight under a long black skirt and behind the Volvo's open door – a man was waiting to get past in his car. Mike managed to disentangle Katie and scoop her up into his jumper while the motorist threw his arms wide in a frustrated gesture as if to say: "Could I get past, please?"

We squeezed ourselves closer to the car and I will never forget the man's face as he edged slowly past.

Mike said: "It's a girl. We've got another little girl."

Finally, we had a midwife too, in the angelic form of Julie Godwin who arrived with the ambulance. "Where's the pregnant lady?" she demanded, brushing Mike and baby aside. Her expression also changed rapidly when she realised Katie had already been born and, while she cut the cord to disentangle our new arrival from my skirt, Mike was instructed to get a bucket of water to wash down the road!

Diane Harris

■ ■ ■ It was 4am on January 31, 1999 and I rushed to the bathroom thinking: "Oh no, what have I done?" I got back into bed and closed my eyes but cold fear ran through me – that was NOT wee! My waters had broken – this was it. First priority, make-up. Sitting on a towel, I carefully spread out my make-up bag and AARGHH, contraction No 1: painful, but not too bad.

At 4.05am I said: "Wake up Martin, the baby's coming." I shook him, poked him, and screamed at him. "Uh what?" came a confused murmur. "WHAT?" he shouted and jumped out of bed.

I calmly walked down the stairs with the towel and phoned SMH. After a short chat, I finished the conversation by saying I think I'll have a BAAAGGGHHth. "I think you'd better come in," came the reply. Contraction No 2: very painful.

By 4.08am I was okay again. I ran upstairs with the towel, couldn't find any clean clothes and rummaged around in drawer. AAAGGGHHHHH! Contraction No 3: worse than ever before. Then I was okay again, but still couldn't find any clothes. "Wear these," shouted Martin, now panicking. He was holding up a pair of his jogging bottoms. "I can't wear those. I'll look stupid!" I shouted before contraction No 4: much worse.

Out of the house at 4.15am and it was cold and dark. Reaching the top step, I felt the baby's head pushing down. I walked over the road like a penguin. I was also making some very scary noises. I got in the front seat of the van. It was filthy dirty, contained half a building site, and stank of old sandwiches.

Rounding the corner of the road, I screamed out: "It's coming!" "Shall I go or shall I stop?" shouted Martin. "Just get me to the hospital!"

Things were a blur until I discovered that we were driving backwards. "WHAT are you doing?" I screamed. "One-way street!" he shouted. It was too late to argue as the baby catapulted from me outside Acre Street stores, barely missing the dashboard.

"What is it?" he trembled, still trying to get to the hospital. "It's a baby!" I replied. I actually had no idea what the sex was and, without looking, put the baby inside my coat as it was freezing. Time check: 4.20am.

Eventually we reached SMH, missing the corner of the building by inches. There was my frantic husband, our dirty old car and me clutching a small person on a string. I watched him run down the path, press the bell and gibber at the confused midwife on the other end. A minute later two midwives and a wheelchair accompanied my husband, who was nearly crying. Meanwhile, I was feeling fine. After being transferred to the chair I was taken to the delivery suite. Martin shook uncontrollably as they made him a cup of tea.

"It's a girl," they announced. It was now 4.28am. Phew, I thought, thank God that's over! The whole 20 minutes had been surreal. She – Molly – was beautiful and it wasn't over, it had only just begun. Thank goodness SMH was there. My driver would never have made it to Gloucester!

Rachael Neary-Pegler

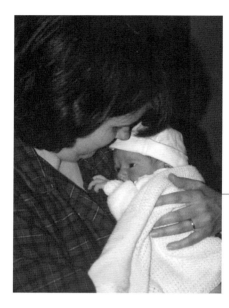

*Sarah with baby
Edward Berry*

■ ■ ■ My contractions started at 3.30 one morning in February 2002. I didn't like to wake anyone but by 4.30 they really hurt and at about 5am my waters went. I phoned my mum to come and get my daughter Emma and we phoned for an ambulance, which came at 5.30. Edward was born at 5.50.

He came really quickly. We had to call an ambulance because I didn't think I could go in a car. But it was not much fun going head first down Toadsmoor at 60mph. As it happened he was born in the ambulance, in the car park, outside SMH with the doors wide open.

It was really scary. I think it was much worse than having a longer labour. The ambulance hadn't contacted the hospital to say I was on my way, so I had to ring the doorbell, with Edward still attached under my dressing gown. I think the ambulance men were more scared than I was. But once I got inside the hospital and had delivered the placenta, it was lovely and by 6.30am we were all right again. The care at SMH was fantastic. I had Emma there too and I couldn't fault it at all.

Sarah Berry

■ ■ ■ An ambulance man came in with a baby and handed it to me, saying he needed a cup of tea and what a lovely boy the baby was and to let him know if he was all right.

Well I washed the baby and it wasn't a boy. It was a girl with a very long cord between her legs. I told the ambulance man: "You and me need to have a little chat." I had to show him the baby was a girl because he wouldn't believe me.

Nursery Nurse June Strange

12 · WATER BABIES

Y DAUGHTER WAS born in October 1993, and as far as we know she was the first water birth at SMH.

Unfortunately, it did not go entirely according to plan. When we arrived at the hospital the hired water birthing tank had been assembled but the staff could only find a small gauge hose with which to fill it.

After an hour or so there was still only a tiny trickle of water in the tank and my wife, Bridget, was already quite dilated so an ordinary bath was run for her and she got in. There then followed a frantic scene in which the male midwife and I filled dozens of buckets of water, using every available basin in the hospital, running backwards and forwards with them trying to fill the tank.

It was like a scene from a Buster Keaton film. There was water slopping everywhere across the floors. Meanwhile, Bridget was relaxing quite nicely in the hot bath and when the tank was finally ready she was feeling so dopey she didn't want to be moved. For a moment the midwife even considered delivering the baby in the confines of the small bath, but that was not really possible.

Finally, Bridget was assisted, dripping wet, from bath to birthing tank, and from then the birth went well. It was a miracle to see our tiny daughter emerge underwater, remaining immersed for a few seconds, and I'm sure that experience has been instrumental in her being such a strong swimmer.

The staff at Stroud were fantastic when both our children were born. It's a cosy, intimate place and I'm sure many other parents have good memories.

James Milroy

■ ■ ■ I remember one of the first water births I attended when we had a portable pool, which was a framed tent affair. The lady was doing great and the husband suddenly disappeared and came back with his swimming trunks on and got into the pool with her. I wasn't quite expecting that!

I also remember one home birth when we used great big pasta pans to fill the pool. We used a hose to fill up the pool but because it took half an hour and the lady was getting on very quickly, one of the GPs used the pans in a bid to get enough water in the pool.

Before Weavers Croft was built, you could see the paddock from the windows, and I used to think how peaceful it was for women in labour. I still think the hospital has a wonderful peaceful quality about it and am sure women get on well in labour because of that.

Midwife Sue Ballinger

▨ ▨ ▨ The first water birth I did was in a fishpond which had been bought by a patient. The pond was supported on milk crates and neither the patient, the student nor myself knew what we were doing, but we muddled through. We all took photos at various points during the delivery and it was a lovely birth.

The water births have been patient-led – the mothers have wanted to have their babies in water and the midwives have gone along with it. We had a portable pool, which we used to fill with buckets. It used to take us hours to fill up, but then the League of Friends came to our rescue. The midwives raised £3,000 and the Friends helped us pay for the rest and we now have an installed water pool.

Clinical Midwifery Manager Debbie Harrison

James Hamilton and Bridget Tibbs with their water baby, Noah, born in the birthing pool at SMH on May 10, 2000. Bridget also had a water birth with their second son, Zachary, on December 2, 2001

13 · FATHER FIGURES

DADS HAVE NOTICED vast changes in SMH's 50-year history – from the times when men were actively discouraged from being in the hospital, never mind by the mother's side, and when they only got to view their newborns for a few minutes through the nursery window, to modern times when they are invited to help fill the birthing pool and cut the cord.

■ ■ ■ My wife, Pamela, stayed in about two weeks after John's birth on October 15, 1953. I wasn't allowed to hold him for the first three days. All the dads had to stand in the corridor and the nurses held the babies up at the windows. Nobody was allowed in where the babies were – only the staff – so you couldn't go in and hold them.

One time I heard a nurse say: "That's not the right baby!" Evidently they were holding up two babies and I was looking at the wrong one.

Charlie Gaston

John Gaston as a baby

■ ■ ■ After my birth in 1953 I found myself back there 49 years later when my son, Leon, arrived on December 15, 2002. I was the first to hold him. I was allowed to cut the cord and the midwife gave him to me. The staff were absolutely brilliant and really looked after Leon and my partner, Mel, who didn't want to leave.

John Gaston

▨ ▨ ▨ Our eldest daughter, Louise, was born at SMH on October 19, 1964 – our first wedding anniversary – but they didn't encourage dads to be at the birth. Their attitude was a bit that husbands got in the way. We were just visitors really. We had been staying with Diane's parents when she went into SMH with Louise, because our new house was four or five months late in completion. I managed, with the help of relatives and friends, to have it ready just in time to move in when Diane came out of SMH.

I saw Andrea born in September 1967 because it was at home, in our bedroom. Nurse Hatherall delivered her. She was one of the old school. She said to me: "Don't just stand there, come and help." So I was fetching towels or water or something.

Ron Gardiner

▨ ▨ ▨ My wife gave birth to our eldest in Stroud in 1972. We vividly recall the matron in grey. Most of the time, the babies were kept in a separate room and during visiting hours she would ring a bell to signal the small period of time fathers were allowed to see their little ones. On one occasion my mother-in-law ventured into the room with me only to be removed and reprimanded by matron as it was strictly dads only. How different it all is now.

I wasn't at the birth. If I recall correctly it wasn't the done thing for fathers to be present. Babies were then taken off into a separate room. It was so different when my other two children were born eight and 10 years later. I was at the birth for both, although I fainted when our second son arrived.

Richard Barnard

▨ ▨ ▨ As a father of two babies born at SMH I think both mothers and fathers benefit from its facilities. Like most dads I work, and had to juggle things to make sure when the pregnancy was reaching its conclusion I was able to support Marianne as much as she needed.

I would have seriously dreaded the thought of 30-mile round trips to Gloucester during the first few days of family life.

Abigail's birth was a two-stage affair which seemed to go well at first, but there then followed a lot of effort with little result and I found myself not quite sure if I should be hanging about or doing something else. Because SMH is so relaxed, there was never any pressure on me to get out or involved, and I never felt in the way. I found the atmosphere comforting.

I recall one moment when the consultant suggested Marianne may have to think about getting in an ambulance to be ferried to Gloucester. Apart from the limited chances of convincing Marianne, I thought SMH staff were doing the right thing to ensure nature took its course and that mother and baby would get there eventually.

It really is the people who make the unit special – the time taken to help women prepare for motherhood and returning home.

When Abigail was less than one year old, I had to go to Gloucester for an appendix removal. I can still recall the strange isolation you feel in a big hospital and it's not something I would wish upon any mother at such a potentially vulnerable time.

Pete King

■ ■ ■ You are always a bit hypersensitive and jumpy with your first child and we had a false alarm in the middle of the night when my wife, Helen, was expecting Hannah in 1995. We leapt into action, got straight into the car and drove off in a first-time parents' panic.

At the time I had a high-powered sporty BMW, like a drug dealer's car. So it was no surprise as we bombed down from Bussage and along the A419 at something like 75mph at 2am that we attracted the attention of the local constabulary.

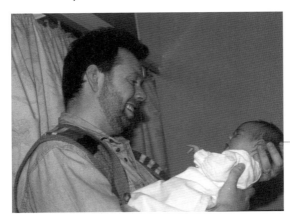

Adrian Leatherland with daughter Hannah

As soon as I spotted the police car I slowed right down, of course, and they came up behind us. They followed on our tail, all the way to the hospital, remaining about six inches from our bumper. As we turned into SMH, they pulled over on the road outside, and only drove away when they saw a very obviously expectant Helen emerge from our car. They looked a bit sheepish so we waved and smiled.

Adrian Leatherland

■ ■ ■ My dad, John Davis, helped plaster the new hospital building in 1953. His brother-in-law, my uncle Arthur Cox, had the contract to do the plastering when it was first built. He was the first to have a bath in there one night after work and my dad had a bath after him.

I was born there and so were my sisters. Our eldest daughter, Harriet, and youngest, Grace, were both born in Gloucester but Cheryl went back to SMH for aftercare and always said she loved being in Stroud. My son, Ollie, was born there in 1996. While waiting in one of the side rooms, one of the dinner staff came in and asked if I wanted anything to eat and I said I'd just have a sandwich. But in the end I had Cheryl's cooked lunch and she had the sandwich.

When Ollie was born, the midwife handed him to me with the cord still attached. But I told her I thought I was going to faint – I'm not good with things like that – and she had to hand him over to one of the other staff. I felt really ill and sat in the corner with my head down by my knees. Dr Crouch came in and asked me if I was all right. I told him maybe he'd better look after Cheryl first!

Bill Davis, whose late wife Cheryl gave birth
to their middle child, Oliver, at SMH

3

THE NATURAL CHOICE

14 · THE BATTLE FOR STROUD MATERNITY

I N 1997, GLOUCESTERSHIRE Health Authority requested a review of maternity services in the county with a view to closing SMH to save money. The response from staff, managers, local newspapers, the League of Friends and the public was tremendous and unanimous.

I vividly remember standing on the Subscription Rooms' forecourt collecting signatures and crowds of people coming to offer us support. There was a candlelight vigil outside the hospital and a public meeting where women gave very positive, personal accounts of SMH, highlighting how important they felt it was that the service should continue.

As head of midwifery, I'd been invited to participate in the team to review all maternity service provision in Gloucestershire. At times it was extremely lonely as I worked hard to prove that the service in Stroud should

Young campaigner
Abi King

*Health care
assistants Julie Howe
and Maureen
Tucker plus
midwives Sue Hill
and Jo Moon put
their best feet
forward*

be kept and developed. I did, however, receive much support from managers within the Severn NHS Trust, who recognised the hard work the midwives were putting in to offer an exceptional service. I also received many phone calls of support from units across the country in similar positions.

I'm not sure what proved to be the turning point: the public support and 30,000 signature petition, the financial information that showed few

*Graham Furley, of the league of friends, with his beloved VW Beetle
which he used while relaying the campaign message*

savings would be made, the support of Stroud MP David Drew, the impending election or the gradual backing of consultant obstetrician members of the review team. But in July 1998, we heard that we had been successful and the hospital was being given two years to meet specific targets. It was to become midwife-led and a target was set to increase deliveries to 350 per year and post-natal transfers to the same figure.

The news that it should be midwife-led was extremely important as women booking into SMH previously could only do so with the support of their GP. From then on it required only the support of a midwife and therefore opened up the use of the facilities to a much wider group of women. By the end of that year we had hit the target for post-natal transfers and were well on the way to achieving the target for deliveries.

SMH's former Head of Midwifery Cecily Cook

I was concerned when targets were set for the number of deliveries in SMH and transfers back there. The main problem with trying to achieve a certain figure is that the dice have been loaded against the unit, with some GPs unwilling to book women to give birth there.

Consultants and GPs should spell out the alternatives to mothers. The wariness of some GPs to say they support SMH has always been a disappointment. In reality, not only are some women not given any choice, but many are still counselled against SMH when it could be the best facility for them.

My sons Laurence and Chris were born at SMH while our youngest daughter was born at home with the help of midwives from the unit. It is much more personalised and relaxed than larger hospitals and it's also incredibly supportive. You really do get individualised care, which is what new mothers need and want.

We have developed this incredible Western attitude that childbirth is an illness which becomes medically dependent. In other parts of the less-developed world, childbirth is a very natural occurrence.

Mothers-to-be should be free to choose a maternity unit or a home birth, provided the proper support is available through a skilled midwife. Even if the baby is born elsewhere, the post-natal care is superb in Stroud.

We should trust midwifery-led care as the way in which most women and babies are allowed to be delivered. I really feel strongly about that. We don't give midwives the trust and responsibility they deserve and yet they are the specialists because that is what they are doing all the time.

It annoys me when people assume they are completely safe at a larger,

*David Drew's
son Laurence,
born in 1982
at SMH*

consultant-led unit. Risk aversion is the main criticism now levelled at units like Stroud. But there are risks with most things in life. If you are going to eliminate risks you would never get behind the wheel of a car. It's certainly within the skills of the midwife to recognise a problem and to transfer the woman as an emergency.

SMH is one of only two small maternity units left in the West of England. The reason others have shut is strong medical pressure; they are seen to be expendable. But, when I was involved in the campaign to save the unit in 1998, the projected cost savings of closing it were deceptive. They took no account of providing alternative care at other units and if, following any closure, just a few more women had chosen home births, there would have been no savings at all.

The unit has evolved and developed over the last half century to the point where it now really has become a centre of excellence. We are in a very fortunate situation to have it still.

Stroud MP David Drew

■ ■ ■ An agenda for the board meeting of any health authority makes pretty indigestible reading but usually, buried in the 100-odd pages, there is something that will make a reasonable story for a newspaper.

In September 1997, I was reading a Gloucestershire Health Authority agenda when I noticed one of the measures being considered to help save

*Skip Walker with league of friends
chairman David Miller*

£1.2 million and balance GHA's books for the following year was the closure of SMH. A review of the service was to start immediately.

Like any good journalist, I rang everyone I could think of connected with the unit, including league of friends' chairman David Miller and MP David Drew, and ran a front page story. Almost immediately, the issue was picked up by the community; mothers, fathers, aunts, uncles and grand-parents, and the campaign was under way.

On August 19, 1998, I was delighted to run the headline "We've won!" on the front page as the health authority decided that, in view of the over-whelming public support, the unit should remain open. Of all the campaigns I have been involved in during more than 20 years as a journal-ist it was the one which gave me greatest satisfaction. This was people power at its most persuasive.

Skip Walker, *editor of the* Stroud News and Journal

■ ■ ■ People power won the day for SMH. My daughter Carole was born there in 1957 and since 1959 my wife Muriel and I have lived just 500 yards away. I am an executive committee member and press officer for the League of Friends of Stroud Hospitals and the Health Centre, which played a major role in the campaign to keep the unit open along with many other organi-sations, including Stroud Ladies Circle. As a former editor of the *Stroud News and Journal*, I was also pleased to see the paper closely involved in the never-to-be-forgotten struggle of 1998. It was truly amazing how the campaign, from almost silent beginnings, became an ever-growing force to be reckoned with. The petition showed just how strong support for the unit was, and not just in Stroud. On one Saturday morning, I helped collect 300 signatures in Wotton-under-Edge. The procession from SMH to Gloucester also demonstrated the huge strength of feeling against the proposed closure.

Dennis Mason

■ ■ ■ In 1998, I was contacted by staff at SMH, concerned at the news that it faced closure. At the time, I was employed by the Royal College of Midwives (RCM) as regional officer for the South West of England.

Stroud was familiar with the prospect of closure and as soon as the story broke, a campaign was launched to save it. The RCM was committed to supporting the campaign for a number of reasons, the primary one being that, without the unit, there would be no local facility for women in the Stroud area.

The RCM supports women's choice and recognises the importance of women knowing their midwife and having one-to-one care in labour. All of this is possible in units such as Stroud. The fact the unit was saved and continues to provide an excellent service is a testament to the commitment and hard work of the midwives employed there.

However, the campaign's success also says something about the unit's broader role in the community; midwives, mothers and local people worked together to save it because it was important to them all. As RCM regional officer, I was proud to play a part in their fight.

Helen Rogers

Helen Rogers

Campaign car sticker

▓ ▓ ▓ I was chair of the Stroud Valleys' branch of the National Childbirth Trust when the health authority confirmed SMH was under threat. We strongly believed the unit offered a choice for delivery and post-natal care unlike anything else locally, so we sprang into action. I don't think I came across anyone with a bad word to say about the unit.

I attended meetings of interested parties and a campaign was formed, chaired by David Miller, from the League of Friends of Stroud Hospitals and the Health Centre, and well supported by the *Stroud News and Journal* and SMH staff. The SNJ printed car stickers which were still on some vehicles, including mine, five years later.

We all worked hard to collect signatures for the petition and I volunteered the NCT branch to organise its delivery to GHA's offices at Gloucester Docks. We worked out a route involving the petition being carried in the hands of cyclists, runners and baby buggies. There was a march at either end supported by a huge variety of people. I'm sure that day played a part in informing the powers-that-be just how strongly people felt about SMH.

I can't remember when we heard the unit was reprieved but I know targets were set to increase births and post-natal transfers. We then switched our campaign to encouraging all NCT members and local parents to consider strongly the unit for their birth. I don't think we persuaded more people to have babies, but we certainly encouraged them to have them at Stroud!

Ann Hartley

David Miller and Ann Hartley hand over the petition to Stephen Golledge, of GHA

■ ■ ■ My son Alex was born at SMH on January 17, 1981 and I remember the matron, Miss Marion Light, encouraging the mothers to drink stout instead of squash. I have very happy memories of his birth, which was one of the reasons I decided to take part in the campaign to save the threatened unit in 1998. I don't think people are processed there. It just seemed very relaxed, with the individual attention new mothers need.

In 1998, Alex was a sixth-former at Archway School and he cycled with me on one part of the 13-mile journey to take the campaign petition to GHA's headquarters. I remember getting on our bikes for the leg from Stratford Park to the top of Pitchcombe Hill where we handed the petition over to two midwives who ran the next three miles.

Paul Griffiths

Paul Griffiths and son Alex

■ ■ ■ When SMH was under threat of closure, most of the attention naturally revolved around the mums. But Harry Crossley and I wanted to show that dads cared too, so we staged a sponsored pushchair walk from Stroud to Gloucester.

At first we thought it would be quite a low-key affair with just the two of us pushing empty buggies from SMH to Gloucestershire Royal. But we managed to get the newspapers interested and money started to pour in.

It was then suggested that other fathers should join in for the first mile

John Ganly and fellow dads push for SMH

or so. BBC Radio Gloucestershire carried out a live interview with us on the morning of the walk and when Harry and I arrived at SMH we were greeted by blazing sunshine, TV cameras and a crowd of fathers with buggies at the ready. There were several banners, and the midwives, who cheered us off, appeared really to appreciate what we were doing.

The procession of fathers with buggies and babies, moving slowly down through the town, was a tremendous sight. At the bottom of the High Street, Harry and I handed our sons over to their mothers and pressed on alone to walk the 10 miles or so to GRH with our empty buggies.

We arrived some four hours later and were greeted by yet more midwives and soft drinks. We felt really proud to have helped raise awareness of the campaign and to have collected a good sum of money for the League of Friends along the way.

John Ganly

15 · SUPPORT SERVICES

HEALTH VISITORS

M Y FIRST EXPERIENCE of midwifery was in the late 1960s when women were expected to have their babies at home unless there was a good reason to go into hospital. Today, SMH comes into its own as a perfect halfway house between hospital and home.

I did general nursing first and started midwifery training in 1969. I moved to Berkeley's maternity unit, where my second child was born, in the early 1980s, and worked there until it closed down in 1988. It was lovely, like SMH but even smaller. Long before larger hospitals, SMH and Berkeley made more options available to mothers. While I was at Berkeley we were giving women delivery choices. If they wanted to sit on a bean bag, kneel, stand or whatever, it was fine.

I was really upset when Berkeley's unit finally shut and it was then that I decided to train as a health visitor, qualifying in August 1989. As a midwife I had always missed letting the women go when they left hospital, realising that many new mums had a lot of problems in their lives which impinged on their health.

*George's first meeting with
baby brother Wilf*

Health visitors liaise with midwives. After the birth, the midwife fills out details like the baby's name and how he or she is feeding and the new mums are handed over to us, usually between 10 and 28 days after delivery. We have a very close relationship with our midwives and work as a team.

Both my grandsons were born at SMH. Although I'd been a midwife for many years, the first water birth I saw was my grandson, George, being born in 2001. It was absolutely wonderful and so relaxed, just the ideal birth.

I looked after him on March 2, 2003, when my daughter-in-law, Shona, had her second water birth at Stroud, which again went to plan, with the safe arrival of Wilf. My son, husband and I took George in to SMH to see his baby brother later that day. Both mum and Wilf were happy and relaxed in the care of the staff at SMH. It's an ideal place to give birth.

Jo Darley

PARENTCRAFT CLASSES

▨▨▨ I think parentcraft is a horrible word because midwives are not teachers and whatever we talk about will never be enough. All community midwives in Stroud provide this service and I think it should be open to everyone, not just first-time mums.

On the first night, I usually pair up couples as an ice-breaking exercise and get them to introduce themselves to each other. They usually want to talk about labour, types of pain relief and what happens in hospital. I end the session with a bit of relaxation for the women and suggest the men go off to the kitchen for a spot of male bonding and washing-up!

The following week we talk about when to go to hospital and what happens during labour. I also explain what midwives do, and how the advice we give nowadays is directly related to current research, not what their parents may have done 30 years ago. This can cause family conflicts at times, especially with current advice about breastfeeding and sleeping babies on their backs.

During a breastfeeding session I usually ask a couple to come back with their new baby and talk about their experiences. I also introduce parents to the health visitor. I always take a group around SMH, even if they're not booked for Stroud, so I can explain the equipment in the delivery suite. I also bath a baby if I can because I know some people don't have much experience of newborns.

Everyone should go away with a bit more knowledge. After the course,

The end products of one of Kath Lowrie's parentcraft classes

I hold a reunion when parents meet each other's babies. The health visitors then offer a post-natal group at the local health centre, which covers topics like safety in the home, baby massage and weaning.

Midwife Kath Lowrie

■ ■ ■ Originally eight of us used to meet up. Now there are seven and at least five or us get together every Wednesday. Adele expects to see her friends then and she knows it is her day!

We first met at the antenatal classes that Kath Lowrie ran. For a lot of us it was our first baby and meeting regularly has enabled us to talk through things we have found difficult, such as lack of sleep. You realise you're not on your own when you share your problems.

Without the classes, I definitely would have found it more difficult and would have felt really alone.

Sharon Alderwick

■ ■ ■ It was my third pregnancy, and although I was a dab hand at having babies, there weren't classes like these for my first two.

I got a lot from them. I found I had much more help with breastfeeding. I couldn't do it for the first two, but I was able to feed Charlie for 17 months. Kath Lowrie has invited me back a couple of times to talk about breastfeeding to other groups.

I could share my own experiences at the parentcraft classes and learn from others. They are a brilliant idea and we still get together and hold joint birthday parties for the children.

Jo Villenueve

STROUD PREGNANCY CARE CENTRE

▨ ▨ ▨ The Stroud Pregnancy Crisis Centre, as it used to be known, opened in July 1987. In April 2003, we moved to The Cross in Nelson Street and changed the name to Stroud Pregnancy Care Centre. This reflected our changing emphasis to care and support for women, with any concerns related to pregnancy, not just those who felt they were in a crisis.

We are trained volunteer counsellors who offer practical support and advice during and after pregnancy, free confidential pregnancy tests and information.

Our counsellors also help those suffering after an abortion, miscarriage, still birth, cot death or from post-natal depression. We have an education team which visits local schools and other groups where we can discuss issues such as relationships, teenage pregnancies and abortion.

We also have a supply of new baby clothes and equipment, which we can give out to those who need them.

Counsellor Cherry White

AQUANATAL CLASSES

▨ ▨ ▨ I started the aquanatal exercise classes with fellow SMH midwife Esther Surridge in 1989. I wanted to attract the really overweight couch potatoes, but our first session at the Shrubberies School pool in Stone-

house, with 12 superfit women, set the scene. It was a standing joke for years that we never got anyone overweight or unfit. But it was, and remains, a worthwhile exercise.

We moved the classes to Beaudesert School because of their popularity and we have two groups there every Sunday morning – one for post-natal ladies and the other for pregnant women. In 1996, a second session was launched on Friday mornings at Dursley swimming pool. Myself and fellow midwives Debra Smith, Debbie Harrison and Michelle Poole are now all qualified aquanatal instructors.

Midwife Janet Hellewell

BREASTFEEDING CLINIC

■ ■ ■ I was one of the midwives who helped set up the SMH breastfeeding clinic. We felt it would provide consistent advice and support to new mothers following their discharge from hospital. The aim was to help women experiencing problems or in need of advice on a wide range of issues including sore nipples, unsettled babies, expressing milk, returning to work while breastfeeding and poor weight gain.

It was developed by a group which included Meg Walker, breastfeeding counsellor for the Stroud Valleys' branch of the National Childbirth Trust, and quickly grew in popularity once mothers and health professionals

Sandie Baker, right, with Carys Grewcock of UNICEF

became aware of it. The clinic, which runs twice weekly in one of the unit's meeting rooms, provides great back-up for the community midwives and health visitors in encouraging mothers to breastfeed. We are proud of our success at SMH. On average, around 86 per cent of women are breastfeeding when they leave the unit.

The hospital's 50th anniversary year signalled the launch of our attempt to gain a globally recognised award. The United Nations Children's Fund (UNICEF) and World Health Organisation are jointly running the Baby Friendly Hospital Initiative, a worldwide campaign to establish best practice in breastfeeding. Our first aim is to gain the Baby Friendly Initiative certificate of commitment. That would give us two years to put an action plan into place to achieve standards aimed at protecting, promoting and supporting breastfeeding mothers and to ultimately gain accreditation.

As well as financial implications, it will involve time and effort. But SMH deserves to achieve Baby Friendly accreditation and we are confident of gaining it.

Midwife Sandie Baker

■ ■ ■ Having given birth in a big teaching hospital in London, I know only too well how an individual can feel they are on a conveyor belt where what they say counts for little or nothing. SMH is just the opposite, which is why I helped start the drop-in breastfeeding clinic.

Mums with babies from two hours to two years old are welcome to discuss any issues. We aim to give them whatever encouragement and information they need to help the baby access breast milk, which not only protects the child but also helps the mother lose pregnancy weight and prevent pre-menopausal breast cancer.

Meg Walker

Stroud MP David Drew pictured with Meg Walker (left) and other National Childbirth Trust breastfeeding counsellors and mums during NCT National Breastfeeding Awareness Week

■ ■ ■ I was so chuffed to be able to breastfeed and it was something I really enjoyed. I'm sure that having the chance to do so in SMH's supportive and restful environment made all the difference. I certainly didn't expect to do so well. When you're a 32AA the prospect of having a bust at all is difficult to imagine, let alone having enough milk to feed a baby.

With both Naomi and Emily I came back to SMH for aftercare and on both occasions my milk flowed in on the second night. My first memory of being in Stroud was feeling like a milk machine and watching my breasts turn into Dolly Parton balloons before my eyes. I could see them change as the milk came in. In fact I was so impressed that I turned to my husband and said: "Take a look, because you'll never see this again!"

I woke up in a milk bath every morning. I would walk to the loo in the night and be followed by a trail of milk. I longed to share my supply around because fellow mums were having trouble while I had plenty to give out. Any whimper from another baby and my bust used to act like a hosepipe and shower milk in every direction.

Tracy Spiers

Tracy Spiers with husband Rog and daughters Naomi and Emily

TWINS CLUB

■ ■ ■ Before starting at SMH in April 1983 as a ward sister, I was a midwife on Stornaway in the Outer Hebrides. My eldest, Catherine, was born by Caesarean in August 1990 and the twins, Carys and Gareth, followed suit four years later. The twins were both breech and huge, over

7lb each at three weeks early. I went back to SMH after Catherine's birth and it saved my sanity. I absolutely loved my stay. The world and his wife visited me, which can be tricky when you're trying to breastfeed your first baby. But I was very good at making milk and I breastfed the twins as well. Mind you, I did nothing else. Feeding them was the best diet I ever went on!

A few months after they were born I thought how nice it would be to meet other mothers of twins. I contacted the woman who used to run a club for parents of multiple births and a thriving twins club was reborn.

I also helped establish parentcraft classes for twins and other multiples in Gloucestershire. Parents often felt ill-prepared as most parentcraft classes were geared towards single births. The tutor would say: "Of course it's different with twins," but never explain how.

The classes are a joint venture with Gloucester Maternity Hospital and are held there. I take the second morning, which covers the feeding of twins, including breast, bottle and expressing. I also teach basic survival techniques and how to introduce other siblings to the new babies.

Midwife Janet Hellewell

Janet Hellewell, right, and staff outside SMH with baby Catherine

16 · STATISTICALLY SPEAKING

T HE FUTURE VIABILITY of SMH depends very much on mothers continuing to choose to have their babies there.

The number of babies born at SMH has fluctuated over its 50-year history due to variations in the national birth rate, social trends and changes in the political agenda.

"A lot of the figures reflect political initiatives," said SMH's head of midwifery Michelle Poole. "Up to the 1970s, there were a lot of home births but they fell dramatically following the Department of Health's Peel Report in 1970, which suggested women would be safer delivering in hospital."

This change is demonstrated dramatically in the Stroud area where the number of home births fell from 253 in the 1963-64 financial year to just seven in 1978. In 1992, the Department of Health's *Changing Childbirth Report* concluded that many women could deliver safely at home, and the number of home births has since increased in the Stroud area.

When SMH became midwife-led it was set a target to increase deliveries at the unit to 350 per year and post-natal transfers to the same figure. Unfortunately, the number has fallen short of that in recent years as the birth rate continues to decline and a growing number of women want the option of an epidural during labour.

In the Stroud and Berkeley Vale area, which extends from Chalford to Frampton and Cranham to Berkeley, 1,138 pregnant women made bookings with midwives in the year from April 2002 to March 2003. Of those, 540 women booked for SMH, around 75 transferred out of the unit, and only 248 had their babies there.

The following statistics on births in the area were recorded at Stroud Register Office.

In the first 12 months following the opening of SMH in 1953:
— SMH: 415
— Home: 213
— Dudbridge Nursing Home: 20
— Sunnyside Nursing Home, Rodborough: 1.

April 1, 1963 to March 30, 1964:
— SMH: 534
— Home: 253

1978:
— SMH: 335
— Berkeley Hospital: 97
— Home: 7

April 1, 1983 to March 30, 1984:
— SMH: 257
— Berkeley Hospital: 84
— Home: 9

April 1, 1993 to March 30, 1994:
— SMH: 273
— Berkeley Hospital: 1
— Home: 21

April 2002 to March 2003:
— SMH: 248
— Home: 20

▓ ▓ ▓ I compile the statistics for SMH. From April 2001 to March 2002, we had 281 births within the unit, 85 of which were first-time deliveries. There were also 29 home deliveries and 11 babies born before arrival at SMH. They are often second babies, especially if the first labour was long and drawn out. It takes them by surprise.

We get post-natal transfers from Gloucester, Cheltenham and Southmead and also have some out-of-area deliveries – people who elect to come to Stroud but live outside the district.

Midwife Bobbie Cullimore

■■■ Our four registrars have a strong association with the unit. We always try to get to SMH on a Wednesday. Even if none of the mums in residence actually want to register the birth, it's still a useful exercise as we can give information so they are prepared for our questions when they do come to see us. We are also often asked for advice about names and we do the best we can.

The enticing smell of food being prepared is hard to ignore and I have tried several times to get a lunch, but without success. The answer is always the same: "You can have a lunch when you've had a baby." I think that price is just a little too high!

Registrar Frances Hoult

■■■ My daughter Katy was born at SMH in January 1988 after a fairly quick labour of four hours. We really shouldn't have gone back for the camera! On arrival I was checked over and told: "Let's get you into the labour ward quick". Once there, it was: "Push!" and there she was. Two years later I was back again, and this time it was a boy, Jack.

In 2003, I was still going back and the people, the midwives, the corridors were almost the same. I was always being told by mums who do not give birth in Stroud that they couldn't wait to get back to SMH because of the excellent aftercare from the dedicated and friendly staff.

Deputy Registrar Sue Purchase

Katy reading to baby Jack watched by dad Derek Purchase

17 · MIDWIFE-LED UNITS

TTEND ANY POSTNATAL group and it doesn't take long before a plethora of awful birth experiences are related. Only about one in six first-time mothers labouring in large consultant units have a normal birth.

This means five out of six have various degrees of medical intervention in their first labour. It seems we do not give birth well – or do we?

There are three natural substances significant in labour and birth: oxytocin, endorphins and adrenalin. Oxytocin is the hormone which causes the womb to contract and is responsible for the progress of labour. It is the 'hormone of love' and causes contractions. It is also released while breast-feeding, and it makes us feel good! When oxytocin is freely released, labours tend to progress well. Oxytocin causes contractions, but the pain we feel is due to the pressure and dilation of the cervix and the distension of the birth canal.

Luckily we have endorphins. These are natural substances, similar to opiates, which are produced when we are physically stretched beyond normal limits. Their effects in labour include an altered perception of time, a sense of well-being, and a modification of pain, which means we can cope.

Then there is adrenalin, the 'fight or flight' hormone that reacts to stress or fear. Women have reportedly stopped having contractions during bomb attacks in war zones and it takes a few hours for the adrenalin to subside to enable labour to restart.

Women MUST feel safe to labour effectively. And this is what I and many others believe is not happening throughout British hospitals today.

Circumstances which interfere with labour by increasing the release of adrenalin include:

— A feeling of being watched
— Being told not to do what your body is telling you to
— Being surrounded by bright lights
— Feeling embarrassed, inhibited or frightened

— Getting moved about (including a long trip to hospital)
— Feeling exposed
— Having concerns about the baby's well-being
— Feeling angry

All the above increase the risk of:
— Contractions slowing
— Slow progress
— A prolonged second stage
— Endorphin levels falling, increasing the need for pain relief
— Foetal distress
— Increased bleeding following the birth
— Problems with breastfeeding

When you look at the physiology behind normal labour it is amazing that anyone has a normal birth in a large, medically-based impersonal maternity unit, among strangers. It becomes a self-fulfilling prophecy. Women encounter labours that are abnormally slow, painful and associated with many problems.

If you look at the statistics for small birth centres like Stroud, then instead of one in six first-time mothers having a normal labour, the figure is at least 70 per cent. This rises to over 90 per cent of second or subsequent births. So what is going on in these units to produce such a contrasting and positive outcome?

In SMH, mothers are able to hormonally react at their own pace and, in most cases, have the continual one-to-one support of a midwife in labour. The labours are not managed in a medical sense but are quietly observed for any potential problems.

Quick access to an epidural is not available. Women who are finding it hard to cope are often directed to the birthing pool. Its relaxing effect reduces the adrenalin release and allows the endorphin levels to catch up with the pain experienced. In a consultant unit, the woman would normally be offered an epidural immediately and epidurals result in a cascade of interventions, including a 50 per cent ventouse/forceps rate for first-time mums.

As a result of the philosophy of units like Stroud, mothers are less likely to bleed, and babies are less likely to be admitted to special care units or have problems with breastfeeding.

I am very grateful we live in a country where Caesarean sections are available for complicated pregnancies and there are special care baby units for poorly babies. But a healthy woman in normal labour will have a better outcome if she stays away from 'complications' experts and has care from 'normal' pregnancy experts – the midwives.

SMH and other small maternity units offer women the chance to reclaim birth as a normal, if challenging, life event.

Midwife Kate Adamson

A Gentle
Journey
into Life

The brochure on SMH which was launched in 2000

■■■ Mothers who have delivered in SMH may help form the framework for its future policies. A true partnership in maternity care is high on the Government's agenda and we are keen for our midwives to work with women who use the service.

All aspects of the unit's care are audited on a regular basis and we are always trying to improve the quality of what we do here.

We started off looking at our standards of care in labour. Since the unit went midwife-led, many of the practice standards we had been using from Gloucester Maternity no longer applied and we needed to produce guidelines of our own. SMH's Standards and Audit Group, which includes midwives and managers, is also examining the unit's antenatal and post-natal care, and parentcraft classes.

The feedback we will gain from women by involving them in this process will ensure that the care we give is up to the standard it should be. We have a good history of working with mothers, but involving them in the future development of the service is an exciting step forward.

Midwife Janet Pollard

18 · BACK TO THE FUTURE

LARGE AND EXCITED crowd filled the rooms and passageways when SMH opened on March 30, 1953. Two days later Rosalie O'Callaghan gave birth to Elizabeth, and 50 years on from that first delivery, the unit is just as well loved by the local community, if not more so. An estimated 20,000 mothers with babies have passed through its doors and the vast majority have been extremely satisfied customers.

Very few people have a bad word to say about SMH. It is one of Stroud's most precious assets, one of the things that sets the town apart from the increasingly uniform world in which we live. Of course, there have been dramatic changes since the 1950s but the unit has adapted admirably to them all. One thing has remained constant, however, and that has been SMH's consistently excellent standards of care.

Matron Marion Light in 1978

Michelle Poole ouside SMH in 2003

Back in 1953, home births were still the norm, rather than the exception. Childbirth was a natural process, not a medical phenomenon.

Admission was only recommended where home conditions were considered inadequate for confinements or when there was likely to be a medical problem. At that time mothers were cared for by their own doctors, with consultants on call at the new maternity hospital, in case of emergency. The 23-bed unit was often so busy that the matron, Miss Ida Haskins, and her staff squeezed in extra beds.

Twenty-five years on and an estimated 12,000 babies later, Marion Light was the matron and, because of the falling birth rate, the hospital was down to 16 beds, plus two for first aid. Miss Light told the assembled Press that around half the beds were occupied at any one time but she was confident the number of births at the unit would rise again.

An extensive £30,000 improvement scheme had just been carried out, including an out-patient department covering antenatal care. As the unit was not being used to capacity, an outpatient eye department also formed part of the scheme.

Upgrading works started in 1992, with the League of Friends and the Severn Trust carrying out extensive modernisation work. Once the refurbishment had been completed, the 40th anniversary was marked by an official reopening by well-known TV doctor Mark Porter.

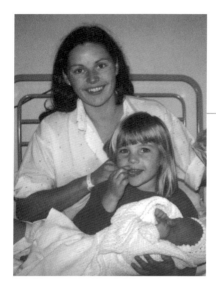

Michelle Poole with daughter Joanna and baby Kurtis

SMH has changed dramatically since Miss Haskins' days, but Michelle Poole, the unit's head of midwifery since 2000, is convinced it still has a vital role to play at the heart of the community.

"In 1953, hospital births were not the norm, whereas nowadays the reverse is true," she said. "Two aspects which have remained constant about the unit, however, are its commitment to high quality care and encouragement of women to have as positive an experience of childbirth as possible, including support with breastfeeding.

"It was a GP-led unit when I joined in 1991. This meant a doctor or consultant would be responsible for a woman's antenatal care together with the midwife. Now, irrespective of where expectant ladies are booked to have their baby, the majority of women are seen by a midwife.

"Since the decision was made in 1998 to become a midwife-led unit, the number of deliveries has increased. We still work closely with local GPs but we deal with the majority of antenatal and childbirth aspects of care.

"All our midwives are very experienced in using traditional midwifery skills, based on up-to-date research. We have 25 midwives, including myself, covering shifts in the unit as well as out in the community, backed up by support staff including nursery nurses, health care assistants and hotel services staff."

SMH has three delivery rooms including one with a birthing pool. It also operates a 24-hour helpline, offering advice and support before and after childbirth.

"Our strength is our homely environment and low-tech atmosphere," explained Michelle. "The unit is now only available for women considered as low risk and we want to move away from the feeling of being in hospital, with all its connotations. Women are well and should not be classified as patients. In a culture of increasing medical intervention, our challenge is to help bring the natural back into childbirth."

Michelle speaks from personal as well as professional experience when she sings the praises of the unit's natural approach.

"I had my son Kurtis here in August 1993 so I fully realise the value of what SMH has to offer," she said. "Women need to have their confidence restored in their ability to give birth naturally, rather than being scared into going to hi-tech environments."

Michelle's challenge now is to continue developing SMH's excellent services and to ensure the unit remains well used so that its very existence is not threatened again.

Michelle with son Kurtis, born August 1993

"We had some Department of Health modernisation money, which we spent at the start of 2002," she said. "The outside aesthetics of the building are not great but the care and capability within it are second to none.

"Good news for the unit has come in the Government's shift in emphasis towards encouraging more midwife-led care and its provision as close to a woman's home as possible.

"We know the Government task force has looked at small units and the Bath model, of seven small units and one central acute hospital, is being looked at to determine if we could move forward in this way.

"We have challenges on several fronts. The birth rate continues to fall nationally and there are growing trends for elected Caesareans as well as access to an epidural for pain relief.

"But there are no easy options with childbirth. Many women are unaware of the down sides to medical intervention as well as the many positives to giving birth naturally.

"Of course, where there are complications modern medicine has a vital role to play. Safety of mum and baby are always paramount and our midwives are well experienced in spotting potential problems.

"But the vast majority of women could deliver naturally by placing a bit more faith in their own body and its ability to do what it is designed to do. It is all about information and women being given the full facts to enable them to make an informed choice.

"The pressure is always on to keep a unit like Stroud viable and it is hard work but the rewards are immense, both for our staff and the women who deliver here.

"I would like to think the unit has got at least another 50 years."

And so say all of us.

THANK YOU

THERE ARE NUMEROUS people who deserve a big vote of thanks for their tremendous support and encouragement, but perhaps the biggest tribute should be paid to our long-suffering husbands, Mike and Rog.

We are also grateful to Stroud MP David Drew, Head of Midwifery Michelle Poole and the staff of Stroud Maternity, both present and retired, as well as other contributors who trusted us with their memories and photographs.

Our gratitude to Matthew Bigwood who supplied both the cover picture and other shots, and also to Simon Pizzey and the Gloucester Citizen, Skip Walker and the Stroud News and Journal and Anna King and Trish Campbell from BBC Radio Gloucestershire.

Many thanks to proof readers Dania Healy, Deb Curtis and Julian Pike and we are indebted to John Shaw and Papers Publishing and Ged and Jason of gedesign.

To local businesses and individuals who have given their support in the form of funds or other sponsorship, our appreciation: David Greenleaf and Bob Beckley at the Stroud & Swindon Building Society, Meg Walker, Denise Gibson, Ken Hill, Dairy Crest, Naturebotts, Stroud Tourist Information Centre, Walkers the Bakers, Sandra and Matt Ashenford, Joan Tucker, Stroud Christian Fellowship, Chris at Stroud Print, Cherry White, Dave G and Age Concern.

For agreeing to sell the book without commission, thank you to: Charles at Stroud Bookshop; R & R Books of Nelson Street, Made In Stroud, Not Foxed Bookshop of Nailsworth, Stroud Library, WH Smith, Stroud.

And finally thank *you* for buying this tribute to the dedication and hard work of staff at Stroud Maternity over the last 50 years. We hope it will encourage future mums to make good use of this invaluable local service and ensure it is there for women in 2053 – and beyond!